This igloo book belongs to:

....

igloobooks

Published in 2017
by Igloo Books Ltd
Cottage Farm
Sywell
NN6 0BJ
www.igloobooks.com

Copyright © 2017 Igloo Books Ltd

TOP001 0717
2 4 6 8 10 9 7 5 3 1
ISBN 978-1-78670-933-2

Cover designed by Jason Shortland
Interiors designed by Matthew Ellero
and Hannah George
Edited by Caroline Richards

Printed and manufactured in China

365

Stories & Poems

igloobooks

Underneath My Bed

There's a monster underneath my bed,
Who really likes to giggle.
He laughs and wiggles his glowing eyes,
Whenever he is tickled!

Mr Mud

"This is the Mud Monster,"
Said Wally to his mum.
"He's visiting from another planet,
It's a very long way to come."

"That's very nice," said Wally's mum,
Taking him to task.
"But he needs to clean up all this mess,
If that's not too much to ask!"

Little Monster

They tell me I'm a monster,
And I suppose they must be right.
And so that I don't frighten them,
I should stay out of sight.

But I don't think I'm all that bad,
I'm cute as well as witty.
And the only thing that matters is,
My mother thinks I'm pretty!

The Paint Monster

There's paint splashed on the ceiling,
There's more paint on the door.
There are splashes on the walls,
And a lot more on the floor.

"Did you do this?" asks Tommy's mother.
"NO!" little Tommy yelps.
"The PAINT MONSTER did it,
And I just sort of helped."

The Great Sheep Chase

James, Lily and Ben loved staying at their grandparents' farm, and always
had fun when they visited. This time, though, Grandad had a problem.
"The sheep are escaping but my sheepdog has hurt his paw!" he cried.
Luckily, Lily had an idea. "We can round up all the sheep," she said.
Both of the boys agreed. "Let's go!" they cried.

James found a sheep running around by the cow barn. It raced past him, knocking over a pail of milk. "Oh, no!" groaned James.

Another sheep had crept into Grandma's flower garden and was munching on her best red roses. CHEW! GULP! CHEW!

"I've got an idea!" cried Grandma, as two sheep burst out of a haystack. "Grandad can drive the tractor and herd the sheep like the sheepdog would."

Soon, Grandad was driving his red tractor, herding the sheep into their pen.
"Open the gate!" yelled Ben. The gate opened just in time and the flock raced in.
"Phew, that's the last one!" said Lily, closing the gate shut. CLICK!
"Great teamwork!" said Grandad, happily. "If you come tomorrow you can
help us some more. You'll all make wonderful farmers one day."
James, Lily and Ben couldn't imagine anything nicer.

Magic Mummy

My mummy can't fly, and she doesn't have wings.
But I think she can do magical things.

No one else around can see,
But everything she does amazes me!

She knows exactly what I'd like for a treat,
She's very kind and very sweet.

She seems to know just what I think.
Before I say, "I'm thirsty!" she'll get me a drink.

If I'm outside playing hide-and-seek,
She can find me without even taking a peek!

Sometimes I think she can read my mind.
If ever I'm lonely, she's never far behind.

Mummy can tell when I'm feeling sad.
She gives me a hug, so I don't feel so bad.

My mummy is special in the best way,
When I'm happy or sad, or when we play.

No one has a mummy quite like I do,
She makes my wishes all come true.

Something Fishy

Crabs and sharks, and oysters too,
Something lurks in a cave!
Lots of fish of every hue,
Seahorses neigh and starfish wave.
A thousand types of seaweed grow,
And when you think there can't be more,
A monster comes, his head down low.
Can that really be a dinosaur?

Ocean Play

Octopus and starfish want to play,
They'd really like some fun today.
Then crab arrives out of the blue,
"Wait!" he says. "I'll join in too."
They play in the water blue and deep,
And when they're tired they go to sleep.

Sea Symphony

Crabs are making a clacking sound,
Dolphin is dancing round and round.
The clacking is making quite a din,
So come on everyone. JOIN IN!

Lobster Greeting

"Look!" says the lobster to his friend.
"There's a mermaid in our cave.
She looks so nice and pretty,
I'll give her a friendly wave."

PJs Muddle

Putting on PJs
Is very hard to do.
And if it takes a while,
Mum will help out too.

They sometimes end up back to front,
Or is it front to back?
And if I'm in a muddle,
I get in my sleeping sack.

Teeth Brushing

This is the way we
Brush our teeth,
Brush our teeth,
Brush our teeth.
This is the way we
Brush our teeth,
Before we go to bed!

Teeny's Birthday

When Teeny woke one morning, he was such a happy bear.
At last it was his birthday and his friends would soon be there.
He wondered what surprises they had organised last night.
He looked around and then he gasped, for no bear was in sight.

There were no cards beside his bed and no friends to sing a song.
This was supposed to be his day and yet his friends had gone.

He crept downstairs and
looked around, but found
no friends at all.

Not even in the garden...

... or in the living room, or hall.

As Teeny sadly went upstairs, he heard some muffled cries.
He opened the door and gasped, he couldn't believe his eyes.
All the bears, in party hats, cheered as they ran out.
Then, they sang "Happy Birthday!" as they waved their arms about.

"Come and dance," they cheered. Then, they cried, "Hip, hip, hooray!
You surely didn't think that we would forget your special day?"
They gave him gifts and played some games, then had a party tea.
Teeny knew for sure, he had the best friends there could be.

The Sleepover

Izzy was sleeping over at Granny and Grandad's house for the first time on her own, and she was feeling a teensy bit nervous. Granny welcomed her with a big hug. "Shall we have a midnight feast later?" asked Granny, with a smile. Izzy nodded her head, shyly.

"Let's make a den first," said Grandad, and he draped a big sheet over the table. Izzy crawled underneath and pretended she was a princess in a carriage. She played for what seemed like hours, until Granny called her and Grandad into the kitchen, ready to start baking treats for their midnight feast.

In the kitchen, Izzy made cookie dough with flour, eggs and sugar...

... then she used a fun cookie cutter to cut out each tasty treat.

Finally, Granny asked Izzy to help her ice some scrummy cupcakes.

At bedtime, Grandad made up a funny story all about Izzy's fluffy teddy.
When the story was finished, Granny brought in all the yummy food.
"We'll have our midnight feast now," she said, sitting down on Izzy's bed.
As Grandad grabbed two cookies, Izzy realised she felt very happy.
"I can't believe I was nervous about sleeping over," she said.
"Please, can I stay again tomorrow?"

The Treasure Trail

James was busy playing pirates by himself one day when he heard a strange banging sound. He grabbed his toy sword and went to investigate. He looked in the kitchen, but found nothing. He looked under the stairs, but found nothing. Finally, he checked his room. There, on his bed, was a mysterious scroll. He unwrapped it and read it aloud.

"On water sails the pirate ship.
Be careful, or you'll take a dip!"

"Take a dip?" thought James. "We don't have a pool, so it must mean the bathroom!" There, in the bath, floated a toy ship with another scroll inside.

"Spy through the glass.
Find your treasure on the grass!"

James didn't need to think for very long about the clue. "There's only one place that could mean," he said, quickly racing outside.

"Surprise!" called James's dad, when James got outside. "Ready for a swashbuckling adventure?" At the bottom of the garden, James was amazed to see a huge pirate ship made from wood. James's mother had also baked a big batch of delicious coin cookies, enough to fill a pirate's treasure chest!

"Permission to come aboard, captain?" asked James, laughing. They soon
set sail and spent the rest of the day at sea. They battled monsters, met dolphins
and discovered treasure, until the sun went down and James the
pirate was ready to return to port, and go to bed.

Tick! Tock!

Tick! Tock! Tick! Tock!
The clock tick-tocks all day.
And when the clock says one o'clock,
I go to the park and play.

Tick! Tock! Tick! Tock!
The clock ticks steadily.
And when the clock says five o'clock,
I know it's time for tea.

Tick! Tock! Tick! Tock!
The clock is blue and bright.
And when the clock says seven o'clock,
It's time to say, "goodnight!"

Five Little Pirates

Five little pirates having lots of fun,
And five little parrots playing in the sun.
A cat, a crab, a monkey too,
And one little spider with nothing to do.

Blast the Cannons

"Ahoy!" called Captain Pegleg.
"I see a ship ahead.
Hoist the skull and crossbones,
And sail full wind ahead."
"Hooray!" cheered the pirates,
Swinging from the mast.
"Load up all the cannons,
And then give them a blast!"

My Big Brother

I'm holding hands with my big brother,
We're going on the slide.
Then we're going on the roundabout,
For a little ride!

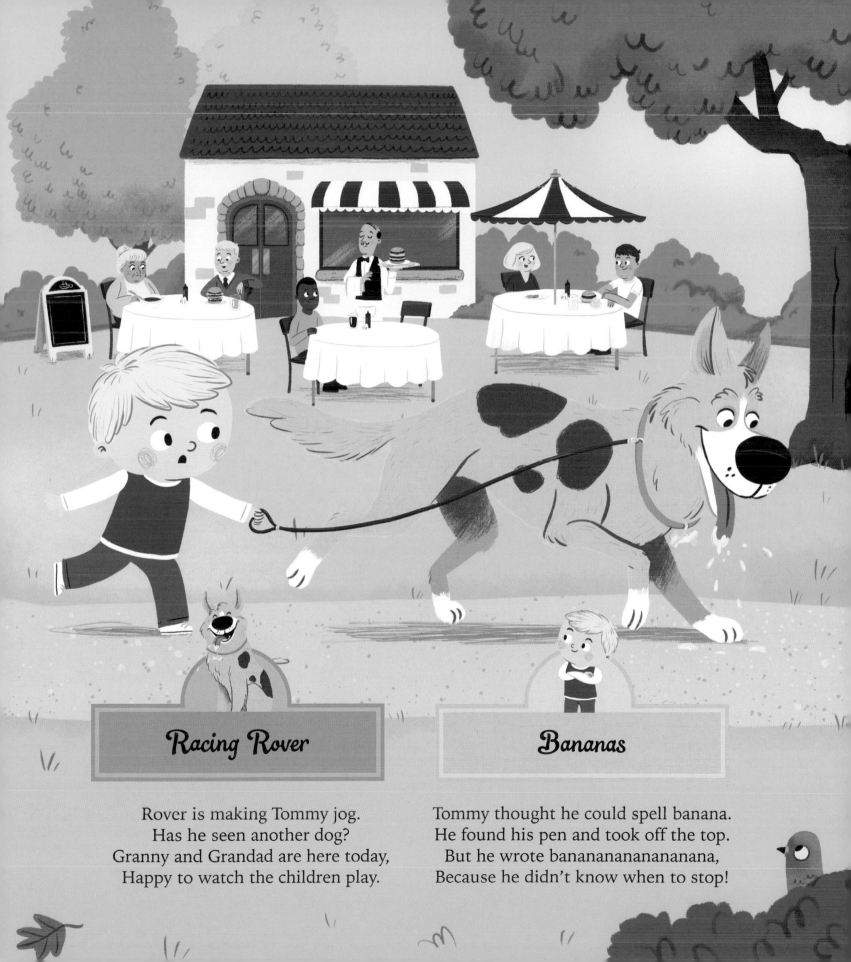

Racing Rover

Rover is making Tommy jog.
Has he seen another dog?
Granny and Grandad are here today,
Happy to watch the children play.

Bananas

Tommy thought he could spell banana.
He found his pen and took off the top.
But he wrote bananananananananana,
Because he didn't know when to stop!

Animal Antics

Foxes, otters, squirrels too,
And a little owl, too-whit! too-whoo!
All have come to laugh and play,
By the stream at the end of the day.

Woodland Town

The animals live in Woodland Town,
Where everyone is busy.
Sweeping, cleaning, tidying up,
Getting in a tizzy.

Toadstools make good houses,
So big and warm inside.
And when the rain comes pouring down,
They're a brilliant place to hide.

My Special Friend

To say how much I love you,
This red heart I will send.
Then you'll know I'm thinking of you,
And that you're my special friend.

Cake Mix

I've got flour, sugar, eggs,
And butter, and a baking tin.
I'm going to mix it all together,
Then put the mixture in.

The tin goes in the oven,
Because the mixture has to bake.
Then when I take it out again,
I'll have lots of little cakes.

Squirrel Tea Party

Baby Squirrel is full of joy,
She's dancing in a whirl.
Mother Squirrel is happy too,
To see her pretty girl.

They're having a tea party,
Friends will be arriving soon.
They said they would be getting there,
In the afternoon.

Nessie the Friendly Monster

Kim and Tim go for a swim,
They do this every day.
A purple monster chases them,
But they always get away.
It's only a pretend chase,
He hasn't caught them yet.
For Nessie the friendly monster,
Is just their giant pet.

Hide-and-Seek

I'm a great big friendly monster,
I swim around all day.
But when I see the Merfolk,
I always ask to play.
We usually play at hide-and-seek,
But I'm much too big to hide.
Whatever I try to squeeze behind,
I stick out on either side.

King Neptune

King Neptune is on his throne,
With little mermaids all around.
The mermaids flick their fishy tails,
To make a swishing sound.
"Little mermaids," says the king.
"We're going to have a ball.
It will take place in the palace,
In the grand banqueting hall."
The mermaids laugh and clap their hands,
And decide what they will wear.
Lots of pretty necklaces,
And white pearls in their hair.

Mystic Merfolk

From ordinary children,
A shy sea monster hides.
But when he sees the Merfolk,
He always gives them a ride.

Magic Toy Box

I love my pretty bedroom,
Where my soft blanket is pink.
But although I may be fast asleep,
My toys don't sleep a wink.

The minute that my eyes are closed,
They get up and start to play.
And they don't go back to bed,
Until night has turned to day.

Little Sister

My little sister Ella,
Shares a room with me.
She throws her toys,
And makes lots of noise,
But that's because she's three!

Messy Millie

My room is really messy,
It's as messy as can be.
Mum says if I don't clean up,
I can't have any tea!

Captain Awesome

My name is Captain Awesome,
I go where there is trouble.
I help when there's an earthquake,
And lift people out of rubble.
I hold back avalanches,
As all superheroes do.
My dog always comes with me,
He's a superhero too!

Little Toot

I have a cat called Little Toot,
Her coat is smooth and as black as soot.
I found her when she was very small,
While I was playing with my ball.
She called to me with a tiny, "Mew!"
And asked, "Can I belong to you?"
So I took her home and Mother let
Me keep her as my special pet.

My Best Friend

Daisy is my best friend,
I never leave her side.
We play in the park together,
Whooshing down the slide.

Birthday Cake

It's early in the morning,
And we're baking a cake.
We're giving it to Grandma,
To have when she's awake.
It's got lots of tasty sprinkles,
That she will love to eat.
Grandma will be delighted,
To see her birthday treat!

Brothers and Sisters

Brothers and sisters,
Playing happily together.
They always have fun,
No matter what the weather.

Brave Explorers

The sailing boat is stuck in the sand,
There is no sea, only land!
Jim is in the jungle, he's okay,
And Rob is in space far, far away.
Nina explores a dark and deep cave,
While a pilot flies by and gives a wave.
They will not stop until they're done,
Brave explorers, everyone.

Two Little Brothers

Two little brothers,
Their names are James and John.
John is messing with his tea,
James has his pyjamas on.

John is dropping custard,
From a little spoon.
While James throws his peas,
Aiming at the moon.

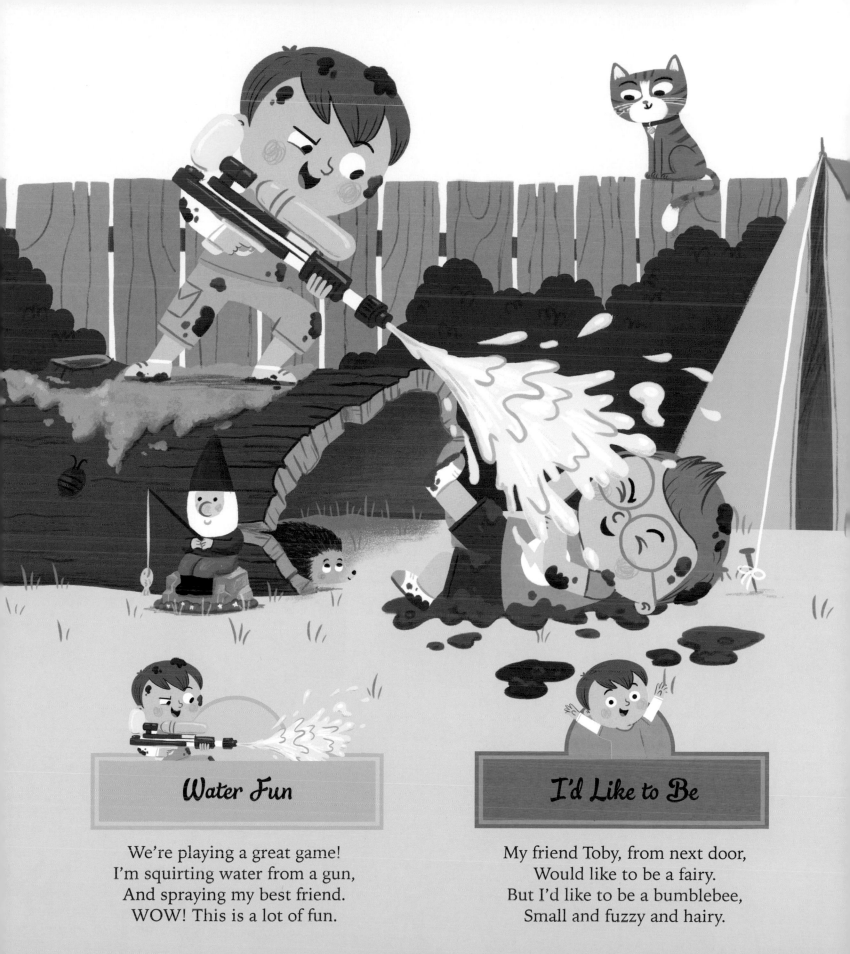

Water Fun

We're playing a great game!
I'm squirting water from a gun,
And spraying my best friend.
WOW! This is a lot of fun.

I'd Like to Be

My friend Toby, from next door,
Would like to be a fairy.
But I'd like to be a bumblebee,
Small and fuzzy and hairy.

Butterfly

Pretty little butterfly,
Fluttering in the air.
As pretty as the flowers,
That are growing everywhere.

Your colours are amazing,
Pink and yellow and blue.
I love you little butterfly,
And everyone else does too.

Flower Picking

Everyone is happy,
It's such a lovely day.
All the woodland creatures
Are coming out to play.
They've come to join the party,
In this woodland glade.
And watch as little fairies
Pick flowers in the shade.

Party Puppy

WOOF! I'm at a birthday party,
And I'm being very good.
Just keeping still and waiting,
For more delicious food.
I'm sitting next to Mia,
Who is my very best friend.
I hope this special party
Will never, ever end.

Fun in the Sun

What a lovely party,
I'm joining in the fun.
I've got a special party hat,
So I can sit out in the sun.

Superhero Sam

Sam is a superhero,
His cape and mask are red.
He wants to go and do brave things,
But Dad says, "Time for bed!"

Puppy the Explorer

"Bye!" calls Mother, from the door,
As Puppy starts to run.
He's carrying binoculars,
So he can have some fun.

He's on an adventure,
Searching for a treat.
Puppy can't wait to find it,
He hopes it's something sweet!

Silent Snow

Snow is falling soft and white,
Blocking out the sun's bright light.
Millions and millions of tiny flakes,
Landing on fields and hills and lakes.
Swirling round, as thick as smoke,
Covering the earth in a velvet cloak.

Snow Angel

One day it began to snow,
Really thick and deep.
I laid down on top of it,
As if I was asleep.
I moved my arms up and down,
As the light began to fade.
Then I stood up and stared,
At the snow angel I had made.

Winter Wonderland

I love it when it snows,
It changes everything.
It makes me want to run and jump,
And dance around and sing.
I put on my comfy jacket,
My boots and gloves and hat.
I roll the snow into balls,
To make the snowman fat.
I get a big, long carrot,
To make a big, long nose.
Then I dress the snowman warmly,
In lots of Dad's old clothes.

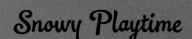

Snowy Playtime

The snow is falling silently,
The birds have all stopped singing.
Cows are sleeping in the barn,
Church bells are ding-a-linging.
The horse is in his stable,
He'll be there most of the day.
Only grown-ups and children,
Will be going out to play.

Farmyard Fun

Milo was staying at his Uncle Dan's farm and was very excited to help.
"First," said Uncle Dan. "I need you to feed the chickens in the shed."
"That sounds really fun!" said Milo, finding a big bucket of feed.
"Oh, and one more thing," said Uncle Dan. "Don't forget to
close the shed door when you are done."

The chickens clucked happily as Milo went into the shed.
In no time at all, the food was gone and the bucket was empty.
"You really were hungry," said Milo. "I had better go and find Uncle Dan."
He said goodbye to the chickens and left, forgetting to shut the shed door.
"Oh, no!" cried Milo, as the chickens escaped. "They're getting away!"

Milo chased the chickens into the field. SPLOSH! He splashed into the water trough. "I'm soaking wet!" he cried.

Milo wasn't giving up that easily. "Come back here you," he called out. SPLAT! He landed in the muddy pigsty.

The chickens ran round and round until, finally, they grew tired. One by one, Milo took them back to the shed.

When he was done, Milo went into the farmhouse.
Aunt May had made a delicious cranberry pie for dinner.
"Better luck on the farm tomorrow, Milo," said Uncle Dan, with a grin.
"I'm sure you'll never forget to close the shed door again!"

Donkeys Don't Have Talent

When the post arrived at Little Farm one morning, it caused quite a stir. "There's going to be a talent show on Saturday," honked Goose, before all the animals rushed off to rehearse their acts.

Donkey heard the hullabaloo
and went to investigate. The pigs were
practising high dives and jumps.

The cows were leaping through
the air and twirling across the grass
like great big ballerinas.

The sheep were practising their
daring high-wire act, and using
the duck pond as a crash mat.

And Goose was busy dancing.
Donkey asked to join in. "No!" all the
animals cried. "Donkeys don't have talent!"

Donkey decided to prove them wrong.
At the talent show, he jumped and
dived in mud, just like the pigs.

He leapt through the air and twirled
across the stage in a pretty ballerina's
tutu, just like the cows.

He daringly walked along a high wire
above a pool of water, just like
the brave sheep.

And, finally, he danced just like
Goose. When he was finished, Donkey
waited for the crowd's reaction.

"Amazing!" cheered the crowd.
All the other animals realised
they had been wrong. "We're
sorry," they said. "Donkeys do
have talent!"

Donkey didn't win first prize,
but everyone agreed he was
the star of the farm
talent show.

Party Dress

Amy has a brand-new dress,
She's such a lucky girl.
The dress is pink and pretty,
She loves to do a twirl.

She's going to a party,
And wants to look her best.
The lovely invitation reads,
"You are a very special guest."

Happily Ever After

Princess Sophie has a pink dress,
Princess Ivy's dress is blue.
They are dancing at a ball,
The princes are dancing, too.

Everyone is happy,
There's lots of fun and laughter.
I think the two princesses,
Will live happily ever after.

The Beaver Family

Here are Mummy and Daddy with their family,
They always sit together, as close as close can be.
Little Sister is in the middle, the boys on either side,
Luckily the sofa is soft and really, really wide.

Little Red Riding Hood

Long ago, there was a young girl whose grandmother gave her a little red cape with a hood. The girl loved the red cape and wore it so often, everyone called her Little Red Riding Hood.

One day, Little Red Riding Hood's mother said, "Granny is ill in bed. Will you take this basket of lovely cakes to her?" "Of course," said Little Red Riding Hood, as she put on her red cape and set off into the dark forest towards Granny's cottage.

Little Red Riding Hood hadn't gone far when a wolf stopped her. "Good afternoon, little girl," said the wolf. "Where might you be off to?" "I'm taking these cakes to my granny who is ill," replied Little Red Riding Hood. The wolf grinned and his dark eyes glinted. He had a plan.

Without a sound, the crafty wolf slipped away unseen and bounded through the forest to Granny's cottage. He flung open the door, found Granny and pushed her inside the cupboard. He put on a nightdress and nightcap, and jumped into Granny's bed, pulling the covers up around himself.

Just then, Little Red Riding Hood tapped on the door.
"Come in, my dear," said the wolf sweetly in his best Granny voice.
Little Red Riding Hood went inside and peered at the strange figure
sat up in bed. "Granny, what big eyes you have," she said.
"All the better to see you with, my dear," said the wolf.

"Granny, what big ears you have," said Little Red Riding Hood.
"All the better to hear you with, my dear," said the wolf.
Little Red Riding Hood stepped slowly towards the bed.
"Granny, what big, sharp teeth you have!" she said, trembling.
"All the better... to EAT you with!" growled the wolf. He leapt
out of bed and Little Red Riding Hood screamed.

Outside, a woodcutter heard Little Red Riding Hood's scream. "I'll put a stop to that," said the woodcutter bravely, and he burst into Granny's cottage. "Stop right there!" he shouted, pointing his shiny axe at the wolf. "Be on your way!"

The wolf ran straight out of the door and into the dark forest. "You saved us!" cried Granny, as Little Red Riding Hood unlocked the cupboard. "Would you like to stay for tea and cake?" The woodcutter agreed and he sat in the warm sunshine with Little Red Riding Hood and Granny, and they never saw the crafty wolf again.

The Mermaid and the Shark

Molly the mermaid lived with her sisters in a beautiful cave
on the edge of a deep lagoon. Nearby were more caves where more
mermaids lived. It was a friendly place, where everyone always played
nicely together. The game Molly loved best of all was hide-and-seek,
and she always found fun places to hide from her sisters.

One day, a new family arrived. Mr and Mrs Shark were very nice, but their son, Simon, was naughty, and he liked showing off and causing trouble.

When Molly made sand cakes, Simon swam in her way and made a big whoosh with his tail. He did exactly the same when she made pretty seashell pictures with her sisters. Molly tried telling Simon off, but all he did was laugh loudly and stick out his tongue.

Simon couldn't stop being naughty. He filled the mermaid's school with stinky seaweed and dropped jellyfish on their heads. He tied Molly's tail to a rock and chased her sisters around the lagoon, all the time laughing and blowing bubbles.

Then Molly thought of a plan. "Catch me if you can!" she called to Simon, one day, and darted off through the caves towards a hole in a big rock. Simon laughed and swam into the hole, after her.

As soon as Molly's sisters saw Simon, they tied a rope with
a bell attached to it around his neck. Now it was Molly's turn
to laugh. "You can't creep up on us now, Simon," she told him.
"We will hear you coming every time."

"Please take the rope off, Molly," pleaded Simon. "I promise
I won't be naughty again." Molly believed him. She removed the
rope and, in time, she and Simon became good friends, and everyone
was happy again. Simon even played hide-and-seek, too.

Treasure Hunters

Raise the sails and fetch the map,
It's time to search for gold.
But don't forget your pirate coat,
In case it gets too cold!

Walk the Plank

Who stole the cookies from Captain Hank?
Whoever did will walk the plank.
"Don't pick on me," said Pirate Jim.
"I'll sink because I cannot swim!"

I Am a Pirate Captain

Tommy Smith

I am a pirate captain,
This is my pirate crew.
We're tough as nails,
With pirate sails,
The skull and crossbones, too.

We have a wooden pirate ship,
To sail upon the sea.
And when we're feeling hungry,
We have fish and chips for tea!

Tommy Smith is a pirate,
A captain brave and bold.
He tells the crew what to do,
And they all do what they're told.

Tommy Smith is a pirate,
He looks for treasure and gold.
All his crew looks up to him,
And he's only six years old.

Twinkly Treasure

Some pirates find a treasure chest,
Full of jewels and a golden crown.
One puts the crown on his head,
And refuses to put it down.

They drape themselves in jewels,
And dance around in glee.
"Stop this silliness," the captain says.
"Let's set out to sea."

Baby Leo's Bedtime

When Summer's baby brother, Leo, was born, everyone was excited.
All except for Summer. "I can't play with him," she said. "He only sleeps
and cries and burps." Instead, Summer played with her teddy, Monty.
He was her best friend and she loved him most in the world.

One night, Baby Leo wouldn't stop crying. Mum tried cuddling him...

... Dad tried singing songs and pulling lots of funny faces...

... even Granny and Grandad tried to help, but nothing worked.

Summer wanted to shut out the noise. She put her head under her pillow. Then she hid under the duvet. She even put her fingers in her ears, but she could still hear Baby Leo. "He does sound very upset," she said to Monty. So she got out of bed and went to see if she could help.

Summer wanted to shut out the noise. She put her head under her pillow.
Then she hid under the duvet. She even put her fingers in her ears, but she
could still hear Baby Leo. "He does sound very upset," she said to Monty.
So she got out of bed and went to see if she could help.

One night, Baby Leo wouldn't stop crying. Mum tried cuddling him...

... Dad tried singing songs and pulling lots of funny faces...

... even Granny and Grandad tried to help, but nothing worked.

Summer leant over Baby Leo's cot and stroked his chubby little cheeks.
They were wet. She knew exactly what to do, and went back to her room
to get Monty. Baby Leo stopped crying straight away. "Leo can keep Monty,"
said Summer. "I have a baby brother now, and I love him most of all."

Birthday Surprise

It was Mother's birthday,
and once she was awake,
Tilly thought of what to give her,
something she could make.

She got out all her paints and paper,
pencils, pens and more.
And soon she'd scattered everything,
all across the floor.

SPLAT! went the pink paint.
SPLOSH! went the blue.
SWISH! went the tissue paper,
glitter tubes and glue.

Then the birthday card was done,
with a message inside, too.
"Mother!" called out Tilly,
"I have something nice for you!"

Mother gasped when she saw Tilly,
covered head to toe in ink.
There was so much wet paint on the floor,
it was like a skating rink.

"It's fantastic!" said Mother.
"I love every single part!"
The best bit is YOU, Tilly,
you're a work of art!"

"Thank you, Tilly," Mother said.
"It's the most amazing card.
It must have taken a long time,
and you've tried so very hard."

Mother was really happy,
she thought Tilly was so clever.
She was definitely having,
the finest birthday, ever.

Smiling Star

We're camping out with Dad tonight,
The stars are very, very bright.
There's a really big one, can you see?
I'm sure it's smiling down on me.

Fairy Friends

Whether fairies are big,
Or whether they're small.
Whether they're short,
Or whether they're tall.
Every fairy is soft and sweet,
With a gentle heart, and dainty feet.

Busy Farmyard

Billy has a wheelbarrow,
Stanley likes to rake.
Tommy drives a tractor,
But Will can't stay awake!

Little Brown Hen

Clickety, clackety, little brown hen,
Lays two eggs for Joe and Ben.
She sits on her nest, down on the floor,
And then lays two big, brown eggs more.

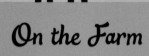

On the Farm

The sheep are in the meadow,
The cows are in the hay.
The pigs are rolling in the mud,
The hens are going to lay.

The farmer is on his tractor,
The dog is chasing the cat.
The farmer's wife is going out,
Wearing her brand-new hat.

The Farmer's Daughter

The cats need feeding,
There are dishes in the sink.
The cows need milking,
There's hardly time to think.
But when the day is over,
And the farmer's daughter sits.
She can't think of a better life,
She loves her work to bits!

Silly Snowballs

Little Fox's snowball,
Lands right on snowman's head.
The birds are wearing woolly hats,
And there are more on the sled.

In or Out?

Playing outside in the snow,
Or playing in the warm inside.
Out or in? In or out?
I just can't decide.

Snow Day

Snowball fights are lots of fun,
After school, when work is done.
Even the teachers like to play,
Before the snow melts away.

Sleepy Savannah

This is a dry and dusty place,
With room to roam and lots of space.
Lion is sleeping in the sun,
Giraffe's work is already done.
Nothing is moving much today,
Only Toucan wants to play.

Travelling Camels

Camels in the desert,
Wading through the sand.
Looking for the water,
They know is close at hand.
They quite enjoy the journey,
And always do their best.
But they can't wait for nightfall,
So they can stop and rest.

Rumbling Rainstorm

There's little water on the ground,
The sun has done its worst.
Elephants search for little pools,
So they can quench their thirst.
But listen to that thunder!
Now there will be rain.
And soon the dry, hot fields,
Will be wet and green again.

Dry Desert

Deserts are hot,
Deserts are dry.
The sun is blazing,
In the sky.
Nowhere to shelter,
Not even a tree.
Oh, for a dip,
In the cool, blue sea.

Royal Pet

Princess Lily has a kitten,
Its fur is as white as snow.
And wherever Princess Lily is,
The kitten has to go.
The kitten's eyes are blue,
It has a crown upon its head.
And when they've finished playing,
They both go off to bed.

Cat Naps

Two little kittens sitting on my lap,
Will be ready for their morning nap.
They sleep a lot, and very soon,
Will be ready for a nap this afternoon.

One Naughty Kitten

Three little kittens went out to play,
Mother Cat said, "Don't run away!"
Two little kittens as good as gold,
But one didn't do as he was told.
He chased a little bird high up a tree,
Mother Cat fetched him to join the family.

Kitty Playtime

I love to watch my kitten play,
She entertains me every day.
She likes to play with ping-pong balls,
And bats them so they bounce off walls.

Smitten Kitten

Princess Rose from head to toe,
Is a princess through and through.
She's really smitten with her kitten,
And her kitten is a princess, too.

Pond Playtime

Little ducklings playing,
Mother looking on.
The weather is getting warmer,
The winter cold has gone.

Happy little ducklings,
With lots of things to do.
Playing well together,
The whole day through.

Six Little Ducklings

Six little ducklings,
Swimming in a row.
Isn't it lucky,
They haven't far to go.

"Hurry!" says Mother Duck,
paddling really fast.
"Excuse us!" the ducklings cheep,
Trying to get past.

"Behave!" quacks Mother Duck.
"There isn't time to play.
We must get home
By the end of the day."

Dilly Duckling

Little Dilly Duckling,
Splashed in a puddle.
Getting all her feathers,
In a mucky muddle.

"Don't do that, Dilly,"
Mother Duck said.
"You'll have to have a bath,
Before you go to bed."

Where Have You Been?

Fluffy little yellow chick,
Where have you been?
"I've been to London,
To look at the queen."

Did the queen wave?
Did she say, "Hello"?
"She didn't even see me,
Because I was down below."

River Run

Exploring down the river,
In a little wooden boat.
Rowing very carefully,
So it will stay afloat.
Ducks are quacking on the bank,
They're getting in a tiz.
Something is close behind,
Can you tell me what it is?

Row Your Boat

Row, row, row your boat,
Gently down the stream.
Merrily, merrily, merrily, merrily,
Life is but a dream.

Little Lost Lamb

A shepherd boy has lost a lamb,
He can't find him anywhere.
"Have you seen my lamb?"
He asks the cat sleeping on the chair.
"Yes," yawns the pussycat,
Opening one eye.
"I saw him running that way,
Towards the old pigsty."
"Have you seen my lamb?"
The shepherd asks the pig.
"He's fluffy and he's white,
And he's not very big."
"Yes, he's here, don't worry,"
Says the pig with a grin.
So he takes the lamb back home,
And shuts him safely in.

Better Together

When I'm playing alone, I get lonely,
so I run to my sister and say,
"Come on, Sis, let's be ninjas or pirates.
It's a better-with-two kind of day!"

In the park, we see who can swing higher.

Then, we race to the slide with a run.

We bounce on each end of the see-saw. Playing together is so much fun.

We both like singing and dancing.
Sometimes we put on a play.
If you do it alone, then it's scary,
but with two, all my fears go away.

We play inside and outside.
We play whatever the weather.
Mother says we are double the trouble,
when we are playing together.

Dancing Delight

The prince and the princess,
Dance the night away.
They move so well together,
When they hear the music play.

The princess is so happy,
As she swirls her dress around.
And her little feet, so graceful,
Hardly touch the ground.

The Ballgown

The pretty little princess,
Is choosing what to wear.
She picks a beautiful pink gown,
With a tiara for her hair.

Later in the evening,
Her best friend will come to stay.
It will make a perfect ending,
To a very happy day.

Swan Song

I was told that when I grew up,
My feathers would all turn white.
But I think it's a fairy's magic dust,
That has made me oh, so bright.

Desert Moon

My brother says the moon is a desert,
Whatever can he mean?
He says it's made of rocks and dust,
Although he's never been.
On the moon there is no rain,
And rain makes green things grow.
So the moon is just a desert,
I've not been there, but I know!

My Friend Ollie

This is my friend Ollie, who no one else can see!
He doesn't look like you, and he doesn't look like me.
Ollie lives inside my wardrobe and only comes out at night.
He giggles, and he tickles me, and then turns on the light.
I put on my best slippers and we most carefully creep,
past the next bedroom, where Mother and Father sleep.

CREAK! goes each step,
as we go down to the hall.

We creep along so quietly,
beside the kitchen wall.

"Open!" Ollie orders,
tapping the fridge door.
We nibble on some
yummy things,
then we want
some more!

We're giggling and crunching,
and sometimes we slurp.
We're munching and chewing,
and can't help but burp.

Then suddenly I hear a voice, it gives me such a fright.
Uh-oh! We've woken up my dad. CLICK! On goes the light.
I try hard to explain to him, but it's just as I feared.
By the time I say, "It was Ollie," he has disappeared!
I trudge up to bed again, this time on my own.
"You've gone and done it again, Ollie," I can't help but groan.

Then I realise and I begin to smile.
Ollie will be right back in just a little while.
In bed, I see a shadow move along the floor,
and I hear the gentle THUNK! of my wardrobe door.
"Goodnight, Ollie," I call. "See you soon!"
and then I fall fast asleep by the light of the moon.

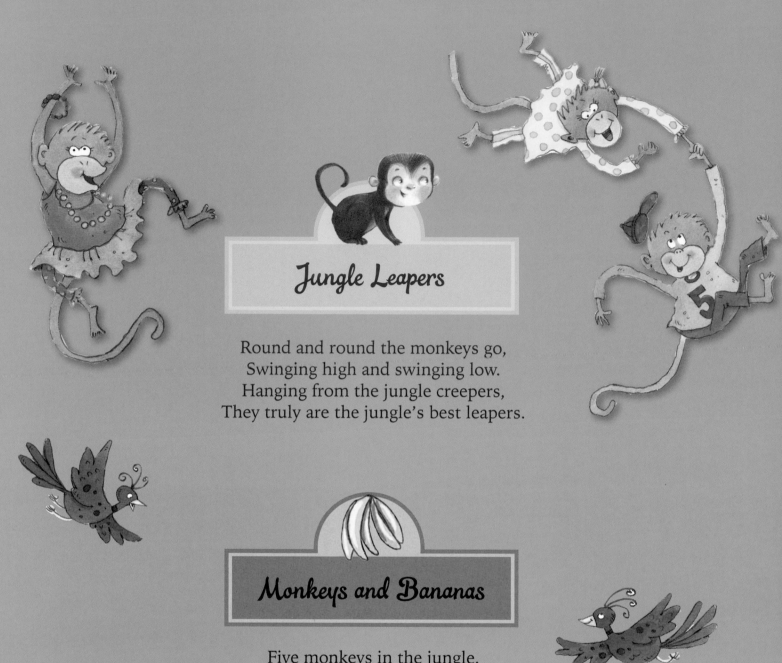

Jungle Leapers

Round and round the monkeys go,
Swinging high and swinging low.
Hanging from the jungle creepers,
They truly are the jungle's best leapers.

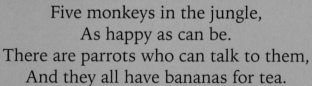

Monkeys and Bananas

Five monkeys in the jungle,
As happy as can be.
There are parrots who can talk to them,
And they all have bananas for tea.

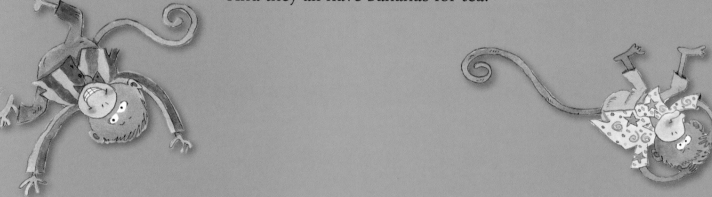

Snuggle Up Tight

Brothers and sisters,
Squashed in a bed.
One girl in the middle,
Has gone quite red.

A little boy is smiling,
Another is sleeping like a log.
And the little boy who's tumbling,
Is falling on the dog.

Dan's Dinosaur

DING-DONG! went the doorbell on Dan's birthday.
It was a parcel from his grandad, who lived very far away.
Dan tore off the wrapping paper and his eyes opened wide.
He gasped when he saw the magic dinosaur book inside.
"I wish, I wish," he said. "I had my own dinosaur!"
Suddenly, the book jumped out of his hands and landed on the floor.

The magic pages sparkled,
they shivered and they shook.
You'll never guess
what came out of the book!

The creature looked at Dan,
and gave a huge ROAR!
"Uh-oh!" said Dan.
"It's a dinosaur!"

Downstairs, Mother called,
"What was that?"
"Nothing!" said Dan.
"I just stood on the cat!"

The dinosaur thundered
down the stairs to the hall.
It shook all the furniture,
and the pictures off the wall.
It ate the cat's biscuits,
and even Dan's sister's toys.
"Oh, Dan," called his dad.
"Please, don't make so much noise!"

Down in the kitchen, the dino ate everything in sight.
He ate all day, and then he ate all night.
He chomped on the quilts and the carpets, too.
"Oh dear!" cried Dan. "What am I going to do?"

Dan wished the dino back into the book.
FIZZ! POP! SWISH! he didn't dare look.
Just then the back door opened wide,
and Dad very carefully stepped inside.

"I know you're up to something,"
his dad said.
"I think, young man,
it's time you went to bed!"

Dan smiled and walked
back across the floor.
Never again would
he wish for a dinosaur!

Little Ship

There's a ship coming towards me,
With a very tiny sail.
I hope it knows just how to stop,
Or it might just hit a whale.
It's moving very fast,
As it sails across the sea.
I may have to swim back home,
Before the little ship hits me!

Animals at Play

Pussycat can pounce and chase,
Puppy dog can leap and race.
Piglet cools himself in the mud,
Mouse would hide, if he could.
Owl will fly when the light is dim,
But only duck can dive and swim!

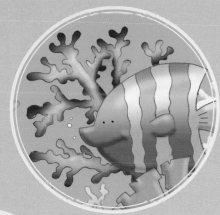

The Bottom of the Sea

The stripy blue and yellow fish,
Swims by lazily.
Past coral and clams,
At the bottom of the sea.
The octopus with dancing legs,
Swims by to say "Hello".
"Can you play," he asks seahorse.
"Before I have to go?"

A Sea Rainbow

Seahorse is yellow, the coral red.
Jellyfish has a purple head.
Seaweed comes in every hue,
And the little fish is electric blue.

Playing Ball

I'm going to the park with Dad,
I'm taking my new ball.
My friends will all be there,
Charlie, John and Paul.
Charlie kicks the ball to John,
John kicks it back to me.
Then I run up and score a goal,
Past my dad, the goalie.

Timmy's Dinosaur

When Timmy went to bed one night,
He heard a tiny roar.
Then out of the wardrobe,
Came a baby dinosaur.
The dinosaur was crying,
Because he'd lost his mum.
"I can't find her anywhere," he cried.
"And I've got a rumbly tum."
"My tum does that," said Tim.
"When it needs something to eat.
Would you like a crunchy apple,
Or a small piece of meat?"
"Yes, please," said the dinosaur.
"Then I will feel much better!
And if you find my mum,
Could we go out and get her?"

Fearless Firefighter

The hay barn is on fire,
I can hear the farmer shout.
I'd better get there quickly,
And put the fire out.
I'll be there in an instant,
And everyone I will save.
Because I'm a superhero,
I'm a firefighter, bold and brave.

Soaring Superhero

Listen to the engines thunder,
Listen to them roar!
Listen to the noise,
As it builds up more and more.
The plane is on the runway,
The pilot waves goodbye.
He is a soaring superhero,
Flying off into the sky.

Brother to the Rescue

Once, my little brother,
Fell and hurt his arm.
So I went to pick him up,
And sounded the alarm.
Someone stopped to help me,
As they were walking past.
And said I was a hero,
Because I acted really fast.

Happiness

If you want to be happy.
You don't have to be a king.
All you need is lots of fun,
And to do lots of happy things.

Hungry Bunny

Roger eats grass for breakfast,
Lunch and supper, too.
He snacks on grass at half past ten,
And then again at two.

The bunny can't stop eating,
He's not getting any thinner.
And when he lies down on the grass,
He's lying on his dinner.

Star Wishes

Teddy wishes on a star,
"I wish that I could travel far,
And see lots of amazing things,
Like golden palaces and kings."

"I'd fly above the mountain peaks,
Like an eagle with a big, curved beak."
The bunnies say, "We wish that too,
So can we come along with you?"

A Single Wish

If I had a single wish,
For every star I see.
There'd be enough for all the world,
With lots more left for me!

Adventure Pig

Pig was fed up. Every day was the same. Get up, eat stuff, go to bed. Surely life could be better? The other animals didn't understand how Pig felt and tried to ask him what he wanted instead. "I want adventure!" cried Pig.

Then one day, when the farmer left the gate open, adventure was exactly what Pig got. Racing away from the farm, Pig explored the nearby woods, until he suddenly became very thirsty. He found a trough in a field, and was about to drink when he heard a thundering sound. "MY WATER!" bellowed a bull, charging up behind him. Pig quickly scrambled under the fence to get away.

Then Pig started to feel a bit peckish. As he was walking through the woods, he saw some acorns scattered on the ground. He was just about to start nibbling one, when he heard angry chittering. Two grumpy squirrels darted over and snatched the acorns from Pig's arms. "OUR NUTS!" they shouted.

Pig yawned. It was time for his nap.
"This looks like a nice place to sleep,"
he thought, peering inside a hole.

Suddenly, he saw two beady black eyes
in the hole. "MY DEN!" said a sly fox.
"But do come in if you want to..."

"Umm, no thanks," said Pig with a gulp, as the sly fox licked his lips.
Pig raced back to the farm as fast as his little trotters would carry him.

Back at the farm, everyone was very relieved to see Pig. He decided that maybe he didn't need adventure, after all. He said sorry and never ran away again.

My Wishes

If I had magic wishes, I know what I would do.
I'd put on my red shoes and come to call for you.
We'd climb on board a magic train and take a magic ride.
We'd have so much fun together, sitting side by side.
CHOO-CHOO! We'd chug away, up to the mountaintop.
Slowly then, over the hill, CLICK-CLACK! No time to stop!

I'd wish that I were a queen and that you were a king.
We'd sit upon our royal thrones, and never do a thing.
Butlers would bring us sweets and cakes on silver dishes.
They'd bow and say, "Your Majesties," and grant us all our wishes.
We'd hold a garden party and invite everyone to tea.
Everybody would have such fun, all thanks to you and me.

I'd wish for a sleepover, and when day turned to night.
We would see a magic land, lit by the moon's bright light.
There, we'd meet the fairies, they'd say, "Come to Fairyland!"
We'd have a fairy feast and dance to the fairy band.

We'd creep back into bed, and then we'd snuggle down to sleep,
And dream of our adventures, with memories to keep.
I'd wish we'd be together, forever and a day.
You'd be my very special friend who never goes away.

On the Carousel

I'm driving a bright-red sports car.
My sister is flying a plane.
When the carousel stops and we get off,
We'll both get on again.
We're getting dizzy, whizzing round,
But that's just what we like.
My sister is on a horse this time,
And I'm on a motorbike.

Home Time

Don't take me home yet, Dad.
We've only just got here.
I've only been on a hundred things,
You can take me home next year!

Going to the Funfair

Funfair! We're going to the funfair!
It's set up on the local park,
So it won't take long to get there.
Funfair! We're going to the funfair!
I want to go on all the rides,
And the scary ghost train, if I dare!

Brave Bonnie

Mother said, "Let's go to the funfair."
But I didn't want to go.
I thought it might be scary,
But I didn't tell her so.
I went on lots and lots of rides,
Mother said it was okay.
I'm glad now that she took me.
I had a terrific day!

Mystic Mermaid

There are starfish on the seabed,
Seashells on the wall.
And the pretty little mermaid,
Looks into her crystal ball.

She questions what the future holds,
And she can plainly see.
A prince is holding out a ring,
Before her on one knee.

Mermaid Wish

So you'd like to be a mermaid,
But do you know what that means?
You wouldn't be able to dance about,
Or wear your pretty jeans.

You couldn't climb a tree,
Or even walk along a path.
You'd probably end up stuck indoors,
Lying in the bath!

Toy Tea Party

Toys just love tea parties,
Teddy bears and dollies.
Eating cake and ice cream,
And licking big, red lollies.
Everyone sits around the table,
Each wearing a funny hat.
And if there's any food left,
They give it to the cat.

Tasty Treats

We're having a tea party.
Cat has made us all a bun.
Everybody is coming,
It's going to be such fun.
Dog's little fairy cakes,
Have taken him all day.
And Bear's gingerbread man,
Is trying to run away.

Six Happy Bears

Six happy bears,
Sit under a leafy tree.
Jim, Bob, Amanda,
Jennifer, John and me.
We're having a tea party,
With apples and ice cream.
And when we've finished eating,
We'll lie in the grass and dream.

The Great Wallendo

I am the Great Wallendo!
I saw girls in half, and then,
When I find the time,
I put them back again!

Hungry for Magic

Can you do magic? I can!
Dad says I have for years.
I sit down to eat my supper,
And POOF! it disappears.

The Magical Bicycle

I am riding on my magic bike,
It takes me just wherever I like.
And although the wheels go round,
They never, ever, touch the ground.

The Disappearing Act

I've only just started magic,
Like pulling coins from someone's ear.
So I was really quite surprised,
When I made your sister disappear.
My wand was pointed at her,
When the end began to fizz.
I'm sure she's around here somewhere.
Can you tell me where she is?

Marvin the Magician

There once was a magician,
Who could do almost anything.
He could pull rabbits out of hats,
And make the moonbeams sing.

He could turn raindrops into jewels,
And snowflakes into bread.
He could make the fish in the sea,
Stand on their heads.

Then one day the magician,
Did something really dim.
He turned his cat into a lion,
And that was the end of him!

The Golden Rocket

Roger was digging in the garden when he found a little rocket.
He rummaged for his handkerchief and pulled it from his pocket.
He rubbed it and he scrubbed it, until it really gleamed.
"It's made of gold!" cried Roger, but it wasn't what it seemed.
That night, Roger sat up in bed, woken by a sound.
The rocket ship was shaking, and Roger's eyes grew round.

Roger touched the rocket, SHAKE! FIZZ! SWOOSH!
Suddenly he was in the ship and it took off with a WHOOSH!
"Hello," said a little voice. "I'm Arnold. Welcome aboard.
Thank you for rescuing me. A space trip is your reward."
VROOM! went the rocket, blasting through the stars.
Roger waved to aliens on their way to Mars.

They zoomed to Arnold's planet, where Roger played with all his friends.
He said to Arnold, "This is such fun, I don't want it to end!"

Roger met Arnold's family, who waved and said, "Hi!"
"Stay for tea," said Arnold's dad. "We've made a meteor pie."
What was in the pie, luckily Roger would never know.
Before he took a single bite, Arnold said, "Time to go!"

Arnold then flew Roger home, landing on his shelf.
And, suddenly, Roger became his normal self.
"Goodbye," said Roger, waving as the rocket shot away.
"Space is just fantastic and I've had a lovely day."
Now, whenever Roger sees a golden flash in the sky,
he's certain it's his little friend's rocket flying by.

Rainbow Play Park

If you want to go out and have fun for the day,
Rainbow Play Park is the perfect place to play.
Grab Mother and Father, and Teddy too.
Then choose your first ride, as there's so much to do.
Play on the roundabout and start off slow.
Then spin around faster, as quick as you can go!

Up and down, up and down,
on the see-saw.
You'll feel like you've never
had such fun before.

You can scramble up the
climbing frame, right to the top.
Go on, nearly there.
You can do it. Don't stop!

You can sneak into the playhouse.
Shhh! Quick, hide.
Then whizz and zoom
down the slippery slide.

Flying backwards and forwards, high on the swing,
you feel like you can do almost anything.
"Giddy-up!" you say, on the bouncy play horse.
Where to next? Why, the sandpit, of course!

Jumping on the trampoline and flying through the air.
Bouncing and soaring without a single care.

Now it's time to go home at the end of the day.
"I had such a lot of fun!" I hear you say.
With so many things to do and see,
Rainbow Play Park is the place to be.

Bubbles, Bubbles

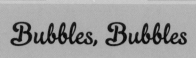

There are bubbles in my hair,
And bubbles on my nose.
Bubbles on my fingers,
And bubbles on my toes.
I'm sitting in the bathtub,
And there are bubbles everywhere.
Soon, I'll pop the bubbles,
And then they'll disappear.

The Octopus and the Fish

An octopus with dangly legs,
Is dancing cheek to cheek,
With a pretty little blue fish,
Who is rather shy and meek.
"Oh, pretty little blue fish,"
Says the Octopus, charmingly.
"You're the sweetest thing I've ever seen,
Please say you'll marry me."

Gingerbread House

When Hansel and Gretel found
The gingerbread house in the wood.
They didn't know the wicked witch,
Would eat them if she could.

Morning Yawning

It's early in the morning,
And I can't stop yawning.
But later on today,
I'll be going out to play.
And I won't be tired at all,
When I'm playing with my ball.

Crocodile Smile

How does a crocodile brush his teeth?
I really do not know.
There are hundreds along the top,
And hundreds down below.
He must scrub and scrub,
And take his time, he never rushes.
It must take fifty tubes of toothpaste,
And lots and lots of brushes.

Cheeky Monkey

Hello cheeky monkey,
What are you up to now?
You've pulled the lion's tail,
And he's making such a row.
You've taken ten bananas,
And hidden them up a tree.
You're going to get a telling off,
Just you wait and see!

Little Hippo

I'm a little hippopotamus,
And I'm very small and neat.
I have two funny ears,
And big, but dainty feet.
If I sometimes come home dirty,
Mother puts me in the tub.
Then she gets a great big bath brush,
And gives me a great big scrub.

Goodnight, Sleep Tight

When I go to bed,
My soft teddy comes, too.
So do my rabbits,
Bunny Pink and Bunny Blue.
We get under the covers,
And snuggle up tight.
While Daddy tells a story,
And kisses us goodnight.

Timmy's Toys

TOOT-TOOT! went Timmy's new toy train.
WHOOSH! ZOOM! went his brilliant toy plane.
WHIZZ! went Timmy's racing car, too.
But none of his playing dreams ever came true.
So he closed his eyes and wished he could fly,
and suddenly he found himself high up in the sky!

Looping-the-loop,
then swooping down low.
There were so many places
Timmy could go!

Before Timmy knew it,
he was zooming down a track.
In his very own train
going CLICKETY-CLACK!

TOOT-TOOT! went the train,
as Timmy pulled on the cord.
He called to his passengers,
"Come on, all aboard!"

In the blink of an eye, Timmy was behind a car's wheel.
"This is the best fun, ever!" Timmy cried with a squeal.
ZIP! went the race car, as he steered round a bend.
Timmy didn't ever want this adventure to end!

"Time for tea!" called Mother, as Timmy opened his eyes.
He was back in his bedroom, much to his surprise.
He'd had a wonderful adventure, with his car, plane and train,
And he thought perhaps, tomorrow, he could do it all again!

Up All Night

If I didn't have to go to sleep,
when Daddy says, "Shhh now, not a peep!"
There are so many fun things I would do,
instead of sleeping the whole night through.
I'd tiptoe along the bedroom floor,
go to the wardrobe and open the door.
Inside, hiding behind my clothes,
would be lots of feet with hairy toes!

They'd belong to monsters of every kind.
They'd smell a bit, but I wouldn't mind.
We'd climb up onto my bed and bounce
up high to show Little Ted.

I'd draw and scribble like never before,
and cover my walls with pictures galore.
I'd watch them as they glimmer and glow.
They'd come to life and put on a show.
Along would come a magical friend.
Our night-time fun would never end.

I'd stay up having fun until the dawn,
then, suddenly, I'd begin to yawn.
Little lions need their sleep after all.
"BEDTIME!" My monster friends would call.

The Mermaid Who Couldn't Swim

Once upon a time, there was a mermaid called Elsa who couldn't swim.
Whenever she flicked her tail and tried, she went down instead of up, and
bumped her head on the seabed. Poor Elsa couldn't even go out on her own,
someone always had to go with her to hold her upright.
"I'm so unhappy," she whispered to herself.

Usually, Elsa's mother went with her if she wanted to go swimming, because her sisters and friends were too busy to help. Sometimes, Elsa would just sit on a rock watching everyone else play, wishing she could join in. "This can't go on," said Elsa's mother, one day when they were going out to the shops. "I'm taking you to see the doctor."

The doctor was a kindly merman, with long, white hair. He scratched
his head as he examined Elsa. "I think the cure is to eat a handful
of blue seaweed every day for an entire week," he said.

The seaweed tasted horrible, but Elsa persisted, and at the end of
the week she put on a brave face and went swimming. Poor Elsa!
Nothing had changed. She just landed upside down as usual.

Watching her was Oliver Octopus. "Yes, I think I know the cure for this," he said, whispering something to Elsa's mother. Elsa's mother hugged him and swam off towards the shops. She came back with a pretty, red parcel tied with white ribbon. She handed it over to Elsa. "What can it be?" asked Elsa, excitedly.

It was a pair of red arm bands! Now Elsa swims and plays with her friends whenever she wants, all thanks to the wise octopus.

The Nibbler

Charlie went a-fishing,
A-fishing he did go.
He took his rod and fishing net,
For bait he used his toe.
A little fish came nibbling,
Charlie gave a shout.
The fish was nibbling Charlie's toe,
So he quickly pulled it out!

Knights of Old

Knights of old were brave and bold,
They were loyal to the king.
They fought in many battles,
And didn't fear a thing.
They wore heavy, chain mail,
When they jousted on horseback.
And a helmet with a visor,
Which was open just a crack.

Band of Friends

Johnny is a drummer,
Charlie plays guitar.
Wendy is on piano,
She is the best, by far.
Clara plays the trumpet,
She's as good as all the boys.
And when they play together,
They make a lot of noise.

Brave Billy

Billy is camping in the garden,
He's on his own, but he doesn't mind.
He has a torch, a drink, and his teddy,
He's really not the scaring kind.
"I'm braver than a lion!" said Billy,
When Dad kissed him goodnight.
"Good," said Dad. "But I'll be here,
If you're worried, or have a fright."

Don't! Don't! Don't!

"Don't eat so fast!"
"Don't run indoors!"
"Don't jump in puddles!"
"Don't slam doors!"
Mother says, "Tommy,
Please don't cling!"
Sometimes...
I just can't do anything!

Coughs and Sniffles

If coughs were made of diamonds,
And sniffles were made of gold.
I'd be really, really, really rich,
As I think I've got a cold!

Alice's Wonderland

When Alice went to Wonderland,
She dreamt of many things.
Of Cheshire cats and rabbits,
Dormice, queens and kings.
She dreamt that she was tiny,
Then she dreamt that she was big.
She dreamt that she was holding,
A squealing little pig.
When Alice told her sister,
Of the things that she had done.
Her sister said, "What a wonderful dream,
It sounds terrific fun."

Little Acorn

I may be only little now,
But soon I'll start to climb.
It may take me a thousand years,
But I can take my time.
I have a lot of patience.
From the day that I was born,
I'll have grown into a massive oak.
Not bad for a little acorn!

The Scared Captain

At the Jolly Jar Tavern, Captain Codcake was busy bragging again.
"I'm the boldest buccaneer to ever sail the oceans," he boasted.
"Nothing in the whole wide world can scare this old sea dog."
The other pirates disagreed. "What about the giant sea monster?"
asked Mad Mick. Captain Codcake simply shrugged his shoulders.
"There's no such thing!" he roared. "Now, get back to the ship!"

The pirates hadn't sailed far when
Captain Codcake spotted something
in the water. "Ahhh. It's a cute
little octopus," he cooed.
The other pirates weren't quite so sure.
Captain Codcake scooped the octopus
out of the water, and it wrapped its tickly
tentacles around his arm.

"I think it likes me!" he said, bringing the octopus in for a hug.
Suddenly, the octopus squirted ink in the captain's face
and pulled his nose with its suckers. "Ouch!" cried the captain.
"Right, I'm taking you below deck to calm down!"

Captain Codcake had only just reached his cabin when he saw a large looming shadow rise out of the sea. "HELP!" he cried. "It's the giant sea monster! It's going to eat us. We're all doomed!"

"It's not the giant sea monster," shouted Mad Mick. "It's an octopus and it just wants its baby back!"

Trembling in terror, Captain Codcake gently gave the baby octopus back to its enormous, and rather scary-looking, mother.

After the octopus had left, Captain Codcake turned to the other pirates. "Maybe I'm not so brave after all," he admitted. "But at least I've got a rip-roaring new tale to tell down at the Jolly Jar Tavern!"

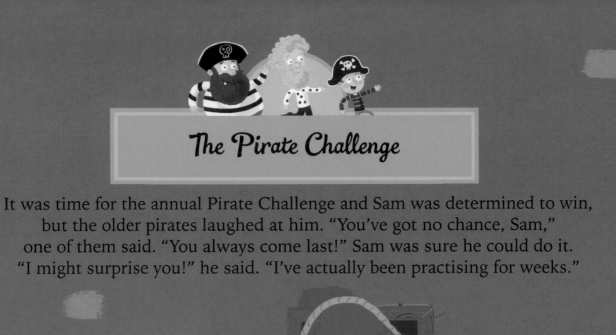

The Pirate Challenge

It was time for the annual Pirate Challenge and Sam was determined to win,
but the older pirates laughed at him. "You've got no chance, Sam,"
one of them said. "You always come last!" Sam was sure he could do it.
"I might surprise you!" he said. "I've actually been practising for weeks."

The first challenge was swabbing the deck. Sam was eager to make the deck shine like gold, but he used too much wax and he slipped and fell... SPLASH! right into his bucket of bubbles.

The next challenge was hoisting the mainsail, but Sam got in a terrible muddle again, and found himself hanging upside down. He then burned his biscuits in the Buccaneer Bake-off. "The others were right," said Sam, sighing. "I will never win the Pirate Challenge!"

Just then, there was a terrible cry from the crow's nest. "MONSTER!"
The pirates ran off, but Sam stayed calm. He quickly tied his tangled
rope to the bucket and filled it with burnt biscuits.

As the monster opened its enormous mouth wider,
Sam threw the burnt biscuits in. "Yuck!" spluttered
the monster. "How utterly disgusting!"

"I'm going to find some nice biscuits!" shouted the monster, swimming away.
One by one, the cowardly pirates slowly came out from their hiding places. The judge
had seen everything, mostly from behind a rock. "We have a winner," she announced.
"I declare Sam the pirate this year's Pirate Challenge Champion!"
Sam was delighted. He had done it at last!

Rudy's Dream Party

It was the night before Rudy's birthday. He was going to have a fancy-dress party and he couldn't wait to see what his friends, Josh, Dan and Felix, would come as. "I'll never get to sleep," thought Rudy, as he closed his eyes. He counted one hundred sheep, and eventually fell fast asleep. WHOOSH! A deafening sound woke him up.

Rudy looked around, but he wasn't at home any more! He was on a desert island, looking for treasure with his friends.

WHOOSH! Rudy and his friends heard the sound again, and they became robots with super powers.

WHOOSH! Then Rudy and his friends became robot explorers on safari! Rudy was just lifting an elephant, when he heard a ting-a-ling sound.

It was Rudy's alarm ringing. "Oh, it was just a dream," he thought, feeling a bit disappointed. He put on his new pirate costume, and waited patiently. Suddenly, the doorbell rang!

Rudy opened the door in amazement. His friends were all stood there wearing
the exact same costumes that Rudy had seen in his dream! Josh was dressed as a safari
explorer, Dan was a swashbuckling pirate and Felix was a robot with super powers.

"Happy birthday, Rudy," they all cried, showing him their presents.
"Wow," said Rudy, staring at his friends' cool clothes. "You all look
really brilliant. My party is a dream come true!"

The Big Red Shed

Animals love the farmer's shed,
It's made of wood and it's painted red.
There's shade in the shed for when it's hot,
And straw to warm them when it's not.

Poppy the Pony

Poppy is my little pony,
Trotting through the flowers.
I ride her nearly every day,
As she can trot for hours.
And when she's not with me,
She has a donkey friend called Joan.
So when I have to go indoors,
She'll never be alone.

Tiny Tim

Princess Charlotte has a pony,
She rides him every day.
Galloping over fields and hills,
To places far away.
The pony's name is Tiny Tim,
He's white with big, brown eyes.
He's very small and really sweet,
He is just the perfect size.

Five Fab Friends

Benjamin, Robert, Jimmy, Joe and Bill,
Are playing together at the top of a hill.
They always play together, they're very special friends,
I hope it lasts forever and the friendship never ends.

One Magical Night

One magical summer night,
The moon was full and round.
The stars were shining bright,
And the wind didn't make a sound.
A princess wished beneath a tree.
A unicorn saw her sitting there.
She waited very patiently,
So pretty and so fair.

"Sweet maid," the unicorn said.
"If you will come,
I'll take you far away,
To a rich kingdom.
Where a prince is waiting,
For your wedding hand.
He'll make you queen,
Of all his land."

"Sweet unicorn,"
He heard the princess say.
"Please take me there,
Without delay."
So the prince and princess,
Met at dawn.
All thanks to
The magical unicorn.

Mysterious Moon

"What's that in the sky?" asked Baby Fox.
"It's shining really bright."
"It's only the moon," said Mother Fox.
"It comes out late at night."
"It's scary," cried Baby Fox.
"Look at the owl's black wing."
"Snuggle up close," said Mother Fox.
"Then you won't be scared of a thing."

Sunny Days

The sun is shining brightly,
Hip! Hip! Hooray!
The sun is shining brightly,
And we're going out to play.

We're having such a good time,
We're having lots of fun.
Playing in the sunshine,
Until the day is done.

Happy Holidays

This is the day we go away,
On a camping holiday!
Our camper van is full of stuff,
Surely we must have enough?
There's so much, you can hardly see,
I hope they've left some room for me!

Come Outside

It really is a lovely thing,
To see the sun again.
To run around outside,
Without the pouring rain.

To picnic in the garden,
Or go for a bike ride.
Or just be with my friend,
Walking side by side.

Spot the Stripes

The jungle is good for hiding.
Lots of things to hide behind!
There's a tiger lurking somewhere,
That you could try to find!

April Showers

Why do April showers
Start so suddenly?
First the sky is blue,
Then rain is soaking me.
Now the sun is out,
The clouds have blown away,
And here's my friend to ask me,
If I want to go and play.

The Wishing Hour

The wishing hour happens
When the moon is round and bright,
And it's twelve o'clock and silent,
In the middle of the night.
That's when little fairies,
Swinging on moonbeams,
Make a wish that children
All have happy dreams.

Ten Toy Teddy Bears

Ten toy teddy bears,
Sitting on a shelf.
Looking through the window
Is a fairy and an elf.
"Is it the magic hour?"
Asks teddy number one.
"Yes," says the fairy.
"Come out and have some fun."

Don't Peek!

In the middle of the night,
When everyone's in bed,
The cat said to the mouse,
"Wake up, sleepyhead.
Let's play a game,
A game of hide-and-seek.
Go and hide your eyes,
And make sure you don't peek!"

Lonely Little Kitten

There was a little kitten,
Who wanted a special friend.
She dreamed of finding company,
So her loneliness would end.
A puppy was asleep nearby,
So the kitten went to ask it,
"Puppy, can I sleep with you,
in your nice warm basket?"

Naughty Magpie

A magpie stole my silver button,
He stole my penny, too.
He took my silver bracelet,
And my necklace, which was new.
He stole my sparkly buckle,
And my box-of-treasures key.
I don't think he knows he's a magpie,
I think he thinks he's me!

Nothing to Something

Some children have lots of things,
Some have nothing at all.
Some have computers, cars and bikes,
Some don't even have a ball.
I'd like to give some of my toys
To children who have nothing.
Then they would wake up one morning,
To find nothing has turned to something.

Peacock's Walk

When the peacock fans his brilliant tail,
It's a wonder to behold.
The patterns take your breath away,
Blue, yellow, green and gold.
As his tail fans out around him,
The peacock struts about.
The sight is so amazing,
All the animals clap and shout.

Dive In!

Penguins love playing underwater.
They think it's really nice.
It's not as cold as the snow above,
Or the water would all be ice!

Baby Penguins

Baby penguins are good swimmers.
They learn to, naturally.
All they need to do
Is jump into the sea.

The South Pole

Penguins jump off diving boards,
And tumble in the snow.
There's nothing like the South Pole,
It's the greatest place they know.

Farm and Seek

It's not easy playing hide-and-seek,
When you live on a farm.
There are chickens in the hen house,
And horses in the barn.
A cow fills space behind a hedge,
And piglets pack their sty.
There's nowhere for the children to hide,
However hard they try.

My Three Hens

My three hens lay special eggs,
Some white, some brown, some blue.
Sometimes they lay them in a nest,
Sometimes in my sister's shoe!
They don't taste any different,
When they're cooked, they're just the same.
My hens are always pleased to see me.
They're so friendly and so tame.

The Zoo Trip

Jimmy, Jack and Joseph,
Are going to the zoo.
They're off to see the monkeys,
The lions and tigers, too.
They'll ride on the elephant,
And see the hippopotamus.
Then they're going to travel home,
On a great big yellow bus.

My Friends

Some friends make me smile,
Some friends make me sigh.
Some friends make me laugh a lot,
And there's one who makes me cry!
I have friends who come and cheer me up,
When I am feeling sad.
I have lots of different types of friends,
And for that I'm really glad.

Five Little Brothers

Five little brothers, going out to play,
Mother calls out, "Don't be out all day!"
We're having pie for supper,
That will be a treat.
I'll be home by five o'clock,
When it's time to eat.

Snail Trails

Once, I followed the silvery trail,
Left behind by a little snail.
Said the snail, when I caught up with him,
"What's your name? I'm called Jim."
"Hello," I said. "My name's Jack.
Race you up the garden and back!"

Digging for Dinosaurs

Fraser loved to pretend he was a famous explorer and was always playing with his dino toys. He dreamed of finding real dinosaur fossils in the garden, but his naughty dog, Digger, always got in the way. "No, Digger!" said Fraser, as Digger made a huge hole in the lawn again. WOOF!

Best of all, Fraser loved his purple T-rex toy and he played with it more than all the others. One day, when he came back outside to play after lunch, the purple T-rex Fraser loved so much had vanished! Fraser and his mother looked everywhere for it, under flowerpots and behind bushes, but it wasn't anywhere to be found.

"Never mind," said Mother, kindly. "I'm sure he'll turn up. Why don't I go inside and fetch you one of your dino comics, instead?" So, Fraser sat in the garden and looked at his cool comic, all about explorers who dig up dinosaur fossils in the desert. "That looks like fun," said Fraser. "I wonder if I can discover dinosaurs in my sandpit?"

Digger watched Fraser playing in the sandpit and wagged his tail, excitedly. He rushed into one of the flower beds and began scrabbling around. Mud and flowers flew everywhere. "No, Digger!" shouted Fraser, as usual, but then, he caught sight of something purple. "It's my T-rex!" he cried. "You make a great exploring partner after all, Digger," said Fraser.

Swimming Lessons

It's good to learn to swim,
In a splashy swimming pool.
With all the other children,
That are in your class at school.

Splashing Simon

Simon loves playing in the sea,
He's learned to swim quite recently.
Dad will watch him splash and play,
Just to make sure that he's okay.

I Love My Mother

I really, really love my mother,
And she really loves me.
We play hide-and-seek together,
And go paddling in the sea.
She picks me up from school,
And makes pizza for my tea.
I really, really love my mother,
And she really loves me.

My Brother's Bike

My brother has a big bike,
Mine is only small.
My brother's bike has two wheels,
Mine has three, in case I fall.
But although he may be bigger,
He's not as fast as me.
I'll overtake him pretty soon,
And race him home for tea.

Moonlight Meetings

Fairies fly on pretty wings,
Doing really magical things.
Like catching stars and painting flowers,
Or making rainbows out of showers.

They get together on a moonlit night,
When the wind is soft and the stars are bright.
Then they dance and sing and fly around,
Making a lovely twinkling sound.

Summer Picnic

"Picnic time," the fairies say.
The teddies say, "Oh, good!"
The fairies magic up the food,
And the teddies chop some wood.

They're going to make a little fire,
And cook some tasty things.
The teddies are going to play guitar,
Fairy Buttercup will sing.

Magical Mischief

The fairies have been busy,
All doing magic tricks.
They turned toadstools into cake,
And made presents out of sticks.

They turned mountains into chocolate,
And clouds became ice cream.
Rivers turned to jelly. It was strange,
Just like a dream.

ZIP! ZAP! went Fairy Storm Cloud,
Changing sunshine into rain.
"Oh, no!" cried Fairy Rainbow,
And changed it back again.

Raindrop Rainbow

When fairies make a rainbow,
They make it out of rain.
They pick the raindrops from the sky,
And throw them up again.

Then the fairies wave their wands,
And make a magic spark.
And the pretty little raindrops,
Form a perfect arch.

Thumbelina

Once upon a time, there was a woman who wanted a child very badly. She wished upon a beautiful rosebud in her garden, and, as if by magic, the petals opened. Inside was a tiny girl no bigger than a small thumb. "I will call you Thumbelina," said the happy woman.

One night, an ugly toad carried Thumbelina away, whispering,
"You'll make a pretty wife for my son," as he placed her on a lily pad.
Seeing what had happened, some kind fish nibbled at the roots of the lily
pad until it floated downstream, far away from the wicked toad.

When Thumbelina awoke, she saw a pretty, yellow butterfly fluttering nearby.
She quickly undid some ribbon from her dress and tied it to his feet. "Will you
pull me along?" she asked. Before she knew it, a huge black beetle lifted Thumbelina
off the lily pad and carried her back to his family. All the little beetles thought she was
a strange-looking creature, so, not wanting to upset them, the black beetle picked up
Thumbelina and put her on a daisy, instead. Poor Thumbelina felt all alone.

Thumbelina lived alone all summer long, sipping nectar from the
flowers and sleeping under petals. The icy winds chilled her when winter came
and she had to look for a warm place to live. Soon, a voice called to her from the
doorway of a little house. "Come in," said a kind mouse. "I have
a warm bed if you want to stay," he said, kindly.

Thumbelina was very happy living with the little mouse. She even looked
after an injured swallow until he was well enough to fly away. Then, one day,
a grumpy old mole came to call and fell in love with Thumbelina.
"Come and live with me in my underground home," he asked her.
"If I go with him," sobbed poor Thumbelina. "I will never see
daylight again." Just then, Thumbelina's swallow friend appeared.
"Jump on my back," he called. "I will carry you far away."
They flew off together over fields and mountains, lakes
and rivers, until they came to a lush forest.

The swallow put Thumbelina down on a beautiful flower.
"Dear friend," he said. "This is your home now." Suddenly, the
flower next to Thumbelina opened its petals, and standing there was
a handsome man. He was exactly the same size as Thumbelina!
"I am the King of the Flowers," he said. Thumbelina fell in
love with him instantly, and he with her. They lived happily
ever after as King and Queen of the Flowers.

Jacob's Bedtime

"Jacob, why aren't you feeling sleepy? Let me have a think!
Try having this tasty cookie and a warm milky drink."
The drink was delicious and the cookie tasted yum,
But Jacob still said, "I'm wide awake, Mum!"

It was little Jacob's bedtime, but he wasn't ready,
So he changed into his PJs and looked for his special teddy.
"It's time for bed," said Mum. "Make no mistake."
"But Mum," said Jacob. "I'm still wide awake!"

Jacob brushed his teeth quickly before going to bed,
But he got lots of toothpaste everywhere instead.
"Jacob," said Mum, gently. "What a big mess you make!"
Jacob's teeth were very clean, but he was still wide awake!

Mum said, "I'll tell you a bedtime story, that never fails."
So she picked up a book with the best fairy tales.
Jacob cuddled his teddy... SSSH! Not a peep!
At long last, little Jacob fell fast asleep.

Squabbling Sisters

My sister, Jenny, is really mean,
She won't let me go on her trampoline.
So I don't let her ride on my nice new bike,
Or play with anything else I like!
Secretly, Jenny's my best friend.
My love for her will never end.
We cuddle up at night together.
We'll be sisters forever and ever.

The Shy Monster

There's a little shy monster,
Hiding behind the wall.
He'd really like to say, "Hello,"
But he's not used to doing it at all.
Perhaps you could ask,
If he'd like to come and play.
Then we'd all be happy,
And that would make his day!

Twirling Ballerina

A pretty ballerina dances
Through the night.
Beneath a million stars,
And a full moon shining bright.
She pirouettes across the grass,
And doesn't make a sound.
Her arms held high above her head,
Her white dress swirling round.

The Apple Tree

Twiddle-dee-dum, twiddle-dee-dee,
A cat sat under the apple tree.
A little mouse saw him and wanted to play,
But the cat said, "No," and chased him away.
A puppy nearby who was watching the fun,
Barked at the cat, making him run.
Now no one sits under the apple tree,
Twiddle-dee-dum, twiddle-dee-dee.

Tidy Bedroom

I'm tidying my bedroom,
Putting things away.
It's quite hard work,
And will probably take all day.
But when it's nice and tidy,
Dad will say, "HOORAH!"
Then he'll give me a big cuddle,
And say that I'm a star.

Happy Dreams

Mother always says,
When she tucks me up in bed,
"I hope you have the sweetest dreams,
My little sleepyhead."
So I cuddle next to Teddy,
And my eyes are closed up tight.
And I dream a lot of happy dreams,
All through the night.

Sleeping Alligator

Deep in the forest,
Where it's shady and cool,
A big alligator is sleeping in a pool.
He sleeps with one eye open,
So he can be aware,
If anything comes too close,
Like a lion or a bear.
If a big fish comes swimming by,
He'll show his teeth and grin.
Then open his jaws big and wide,
And let it swim right in.

Safari Friends

The giraffe and the elephant,
The lion and the bear,
Live in a safari park,
And are learning how to share.
The lion smiles at everyone,
He's hardly ever cross.
He says it doesn't matter,
That he's no longer the boss.
It's good that these animals
Are getting on together.
Perhaps they'll be good friends forever.

Hansel and Gretel

There once was a poor woodcutter who lived on the edge of the forest.
One day, his children, Hansel and Gretel, heard their wicked stepmother tell their
father to take them to the forest and leave them there. "There is not enough food
for us all," she said. Gretel sobbed, but Hansel hugged her and smiled.
"I have a plan," he whispered, putting a piece of bread in his pocket.

The next morning, the children set off with their father. "Sleep for
a while, my children," he said, sadly, and left them there on their own.
When the children woke, clever Hansel said, "I've left a trail of breadcrumbs
we can follow back home." But when they looked, there was nothing left!
The birds had eaten every single one.

Suddenly, a white dove appeared and seemed to want the children to follow it.
Hansel and Gretel were led to a strange little house. The walls were made of gingerbread,
the roof was covered with icing and the window panes were clear sugar. Gretel broke off a
small piece of gingerbread and ate it. Just then the door opened and out came
an old woman. "Hello, my dears," she said. "Please, come in!"

As soon as they did, the old woman slammed the door shut and turned to them.
"I shall feed you until you are plump and juicy, and then I will eat you for my dinner!"
she cackled. The old woman had fooled them, for she was really a witch in disguise!

The witch grabbed Hansel and locked him in a cage. "I will eat you when you're nice and fat," she shrieked, ordering Gretel to cook tasty meals for him. Each day, when the witch asked Hansel to poke his finger through the bars of the cage to see how plump he was getting, clever Hansel held out a chicken bone instead. The witch, who had poor eyesight, didn't notice that it wasn't his finger at all!

Soon, the witch couldn't wait any longer. "I shall eat you as you are," she said. "Climb in first and see if the oven is ready, dear," she told Gretel, but the little girl wasn't fooled this time. "I need your help," said Gretel. "Will you show me how to get in first?" Grumbling, the witch opened the oven door and Gretel pushed her in, then slammed the door shut.

Gretel quickly freed Hansel from the cage and they filled their
pockets with as much of the witch's treasure as they could find. They ran
away from the gingerbread house and, outside, the white dove was
waiting to show them the way home.

When they arrived, their father greeted them with
open arms. "Please forgive me," he wept. "I was under your wicked
stepmother's spell, but now she has gone forever." Then, Hansel and Gretel
showed him all the treasure they had brought back from the witch's house.
"Now we will never go hungry again!" they cried, and the three of them
lived happily together for the rest of their days.

Sloth on a Branch

The sloth on a branch,
Is hanging lazily.
He can't even be bothered
To come down for his tea.

He doesn't move about much,
Because movement makes him wheezy.
So he's going to hang around all day,
And take it nice and easy.

Cat Fight

The lion and the tiger
Are not the best of friends.
They once had a quarrel,
Which is still not at an end.

The lion made a boast,
That he was the fastest and the best.
The tiger answered with a roar,
"Let's put it to the test."

So they raced around a track,
In wild and stormy weather.
Both ran their very fastest,
But stayed pretty close together.

The lion said, "You are right,
We're both equally fit."
The tiger said, "I thought as much,
Why don't we call it quits?"

Baby Monkey

Mother monkey has a baby,
She loves him tenderly.
She carries him on her back,
And gives him special things for tea.
She doesn't leave him for a minute,
She watches him with care.
She wipes his nose and cleans his ears,
And gently strokes his hair.

Waterfall Fun

I'm called a Plesiosaurus,
A dino who likes water.
We play all day at the waterfall,
Just me and my baby daughter.

Gentle Giants

Dinosaurs are sometimes huge,
And sometimes they are small.
Sometimes they are wide and fat,
Sometimes long and tall.
They roamed around the Earth,
Millions of years ago.
I wish that I had met one,
They're the coolest thing I know!

The Emperor's New Clothes

There once was an emperor from a faraway land, who loved dressing up in fine clothes. He spent so much money on them, he had to pay for it all by taxing the people of his kingdom. One day, the emperor heard of two weavers who claimed to make the most beautiful clothes in all the land. What's more, the clothes were invisible to anyone who was stupid, or foolish!

The emperor summoned the weavers to his palace and gave them as much money as they wanted so they could make him the finest suit he'd ever seen. What the emperor didn't know was that the weavers were tricksters! They were only pretending to weave the cloth. They kept all the riches for themselves and sat at empty looms, pretending to work late into the night.

After a while, the emperor sent his most trusted advisor to look at the new cloth. The advisor felt nervous, as he couldn't see a thing! "Is the cloth not the finest you have ever seen?" the tricksters asked him. "Indeed," he said, not wanting to appear stupid, or foolish.

When the suit was ready, the emperor went with his advisors to try it on.
"Feel how light it is," the tricksters said, holding out their hands with nothing in them.
The advisors felt foolish. They could see nothing, but pretended to take the suit.
"It's lighter than air," they said to the emperor. "Please undress, and try it on."

The emperor took off his clothes and dressed in the invisible suit. He looked
in the mirror, but could see nothing but his pants! Not wanting to look stupid,
or foolish, he proclaimed, "What a splendid suit! I shall go out in
it at once and parade through the kingdom!"

When the people saw their emperor parading about the town in only his pants, they tried to hide their smiles, and didn't say anything. "We don't want anyone to think we're stupid," they whispered to each other. So, they clapped and cheered, pretending the emperor looked splendid in his fine new suit.

Then, one small boy, who was more honest than the others, said to his mother, "Look, the emperor is dressed only in his underpants!" When he heard him, the emperor began to laugh and realised how foolish he had been. Then, the crowd began to laugh, too! The emperor threw a huge party for the whole kingdom and promised never to be so interested in only his looks ever again.

The Midnight Mystery

Princess Harriet was having a sleepover at the palace with her best friends, Princess Katie and Princess Sophie. They spent the evening laughing, talking and drinking delicious hot chocolate with marshmallows in it. Just as they were about to go to bed, they heard a strange sound coming from the corridor. "What a terrible noise," said Princess Katie, feeling scared. "I hope it's not an angry ogre."

"There's only one way to
find out," said Princess Harriet.
She grabbed a torch, and the three
little princesses tiptoed out
into the dark corridor.

The noise was coming from a room
at the end of the corridor. As they got
closer, the noise grew louder and louder.
Creeping inside, Harriet shone her torch
on a huddled shape in the bed.

"It's the queen!" giggled Princess Sophie. "She's snoring!"

The girls left the queen snoring, but they could still hear the strange noise downstairs. Soon, they came to another door. "I hope it's not a scary dragon!" said Princess Katie.

Princess Harriet pushed the door open, and, to their surprise, they saw the king, with a pizza in one hand and a dessert in the other. "Hello, girls," said the king, looking embarrassed. "Would you like to join me in a midnight feast?"

The girls all laughed. The noise they'd heard was
the king, downstairs in the kitchen, all along! "Yes, please!" they
all said, settling down at the royal table to enjoy some delicious treats.
"Just one thing," added the king. "Please don't tell the queen!"

Strawberry Cupcakes

Little Sarah Jane is putting icing on her cakes.
She's finished quite a lot, but has plenty more to make.
She ices them all carefully. She hasn't time to stop.
The cakes look really pretty with some strawberries on top.

Six Little Goldfish

We're six little goldfish,
With not a lot to do.
We're happy doing nothing,
As we look out at you!

Super Sport

I'm soccer crazy and I have a dream.
It's to play for a top, goalscoring team.
I'd beat defenders and score for my side.
The crowd would cheer and I'd swell with pride.

I'd love to be a snowboarding master,
Whizzing downhill, going faster and faster.
I'd swish down the slopes and over the humps,
Then fly through the air with super-high jumps!

Driving a fast car would really be ace.
I'd always come first when I entered a race.
I'd zip round the bends as quick as a flash,
Then over the finish line with a dash.

If I could, I'd be a big swimming star.
I'd do breaststroke and crawl and swim really far.
I'd splash past the others to be the best,
And win a gold medal to wear on my chest!

Explorer Travels

Explorers like to go,
Where no one else has been.
Explorers like to see things,
That no one else has seen.
They travel over oceans,
Across rivers, streams and creeks.
And climb high, craggy mountains,
To stand upon high peaks.
They explore deep caves and jungles,
And shipwrecks in the sea.
Explorers are bold and fearless,
And that's what I want to be.

The Pond Monster

Jonny is exploring,
In the garden near the shed.
Something is swimming in the pond.
Can you see its head?
Teddy thinks it's a monster.
He'd warn Jonny if he could.
"Don't worry, Teddy," Jonny says.
"It's just a piece of wood."

Excellent Explorers

Explorers are bold,
Explorers are brave.
They explore in the jungle,
They explore in the cave.
They trek over deserts,
They sail across the sea.
And if they meet danger,
They don't turn and flee.

Dino to the Rescue

"Help!" cried Dippy Diplodocus. "I'm stuck!" He wriggled
and he jiggled, but he couldn't get out of the sticky, slimy swamp.
Suddenly, something red and blue streaked across the sky.
"It's Super Dino!" shouted Dippy. Super Dino swooped down and
plucked him from the swamp. "Thank you!" said Dippy.
"You're welcome," replied Super Dino, as he shot off
into the sky, his cape dripping with mud.

The next day, Terry Pterodactyl was eating juicy berries, when his wings got caught in some prickly branches. "Help me!" called Terry, struggling to get free. There was a WHOOSH! and Super Dino swooped to the rescue. The thorns ripped holes in Super Dino's cape as he freed Terry, and when Terry hugged him, his cape was covered in sticky berry juice.

That afternoon, after Super Dino had saved Trixie T-rex from the rising tide and placed her safely back on the beach, he looked at his poor cape. It was covered in slime, goo and wet sand. There was a big hole in it, too! "I can't be a superhero without a superhero cape," said Super Dino, sadly.

As he plodded home, Super Dino heard another cry for help. "I can't get down!" cried Stevie Stegosaurus, stuck on a mountain. Quickly, Super Dino flew to the rescue, only to realise he wasn't wearing his cape.

"Perhaps I don't need my cape!" thought Super Dino. When he took Stevie back to join the others, the dinosaurs all cheered. They had a special present for him, a new cape! He may not have needed one in the end, but it was nice to know that his friends were so grateful for all his help. "This is super!" he said.

Space Friends

Aliens seem so friendly,
They're the nicest folk around.
I'll visit them in my bright red rocket,
When I take off and make a whooshing sound.
I bet they like to eat tasty sandwiches,
Filled with pickles and cheese.
I wonder if they'll let me share,
If I ask nicely and say please.

Zilly Zing

I have a little alien friend,
His name is Zilly Zing.
He likes to dance across the moon,
Then wave his arms and sing.
The drink he loves is star juice,
And he likes to eat moon cake.
But sometimes Zilly eats too much
And gets a tummy ache!

Alien Visitors

If there are aliens in the sky,
Why haven't they ever come to say, "Hi"?
I wonder if they talk or prefer to sing.
If I could meet one, I'd do anything!
Do they hop or do they walk?
Or do they slither, or even squawk?
Who knows, but perhaps one day,
If they visit Earth, they'll want to stay!

Monster Socks

A funny little space monster,
With a hundred hands and feet,
Couldn't get his socks on,
Without help from his friend, Pete.
All the socks looked different,
Some were orange, some were blue.
The monster thinks they're really cool,
And his friend, Pete, does too.

Daisy's Daydreams

This pretty fairy, Daisy,
Is sitting on her own.
Looking at the snowdrops,
And thinking how they've grown.
"This is the best place,"
She murmurs, happily.
"And here's my friend, Bluebird,
To keep me company."

Best Friends

Spotty bugs and fairies,
Make the very best of friends.
They explore in the forest,
Until the daylight ends.
They play hide-and-seek,
And giggle happily.
Then clap and sing together,
Until it's time for tea.

Holiday Memories

We're going on our holidays,
The sun is shining bright.
Dad is loading up the car,
We'll get there by tonight.
I've got my brand-new camera,
To take pictures of the sea.
Then when I get back home again,
I'll have lovely memories.

Beach Fun

The seaside is really the best.
I'd live there if I could!
I like it when there's a funfair,
And the rides are really good.
I love looking for baby crabs,
And paddling in the sea.
I'd eat ice cream, then fly my kite,
And be home in time for tea.

Grandma's House

Susie is going to Grandma's house,
She's going to have such fun.
They'll play out in the garden,
In the bright, shining sun.
They'll read a princess fairy tale,
Before she goes to bed.
Then Grandpa will make her laugh,
By standing on his head.

Muddy Puddles

Jumping in the muddy puddles,
In the pouring rain.
Getting wet and muddy,
And then doing it again!
Squish-squash-squelch,
Goes the mud as I play.
I really hope the rain
Never goes away.

Rainy Days

Sometimes on a rainy day,
I like to go outside.
Holding my umbrella,
As the raindrops bounce and slide.
At the pond I feed the ducks,
And listen to them quack.
Then I splash in all the puddles,
When I'm on my way back.

Busy Little Ants

Ants are always busy,
Moving very fast.
Racing past each other,
Not wanting to be last.

The worker ants are busiest,
They always run, not walk.
They don't have time to sit around,
To gossip and to talk.

They collect the bits and pieces,
To take back to their nest.
Busy, busy little ants,
All doing their very best.

Silky Spiderwebs

Spider weaves a web,
That is silky and is strong.
She sits down in the middle,
But she won't have to wait long.
Soon there is a buzzing,
In the air nearby.
It's Spider's best friend, Bee,
And she's come to say, "Hi!"

Bob and Barney

"I'm going next door to see Mrs Diplodocus," said Mum to Bob and Barney. "Aunt Betty is coming later and I want the house to stay clean and tidy. No messing about!"

"Alright, Mum!" called her two sons from outside. They kicked their ball into some mud, and Bob said, "I bet I can kick it further than you."
"Bet you can't!" replied Barney, as Bob kicked the ball straight towards the house!

The ball bounced through the doorway. "I bet I can get to the ball before you!" said Bob. "Bet you can't!" replied Barney. They thundered up to the house, and then got jammed in the doorway trying to get in at the same time. Bob was first to the ball, but Barney slid across the floor and grabbed Bob's legs. "Tackle!" he cried.

Bob kicked the ball and it landed out of reach...
"I bet I can jump higher than you!" said Bob.
"Bet you can't!" replied Barney.
They bounced up and down until
the floor shook and the pictures
fell off the walls!

DING-DONG! The doorbell rang and in
came Aunt Betty. When she saw the
state of the house, she gasped. "You two!
Always trying to outdo each other. Now
you must work as a team to get
this place cleaned up."

Bob got the bucket and Barney got the mop. They washed the muddy bounce marks and footprints from the floor, then Bob vacuumed and Barney tidied up. Pictures were put back on the walls, and the ball was rescued from the bookcase.

"Well done!" said Aunt Betty. "And just in time," she added, as Mum came bustling in. "How did you keep the house so tidy?" she asked the boys.

"TEAMWORK!" cried Bob and Barney.

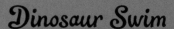

Dinosaur Swim

Dinos in their swimming shorts,
Paddling in the ocean,
Rolling in the sand
And causing a commotion.
I never thought that dinosaurs
Played around like this.
I'm really glad I saw them,
It's a sight that can't be missed.

Dippy the Dino

Dippy the little dinosaur
Is on a stomping spree.
Where is he going?
Let's follow him and see.
He's going to the park,
And sliding down the slide.
He's swinging on the swings,
And going on all the rides.
Now he's coming to your house
To take a little nap.
Oh, would you believe it,
He's sitting on your lap!

Dino Dip

Four little dinosaurs,
Sitting round a pool.
Ready for swimming lessons
At their Dino school.

SPLASH! in jumps one,
SPLOSH! in jumps another.
The littlest one is too scared
And hides behind his brother!

Fly High, Dinosaur

I'm a pterodactyl,
A type of dinosaur.
I may be smaller than the giants,
But I'm also something more.
I can do what they can't,
That's what these wings are for.
I can fly up to the sky and back,
While they stay on the floor!

Dinosaur Differences

Some dinosaurs eat everything,
Some eat Brussels sprouts.
One dinosaur can be very quiet,
While his best friend shouts.
If you should meet one in the street,
Beware, here's some advice:
Run away, fast as you can,
Only some of them are nice.

A Million Years Ago

Dinosaurs are gathering,
They've come from near and far.
One of them plays football,
And another plays guitar.
They are having such a good time,
But however can this be?
They lived a million years ago,
But dress like you and me!

My Mum is Magic

My mum is the best, she beats the rest,
and she'll always be my buddy.
We play outdoors and she doesn't mind
when I get really muddy.

The cakes she bakes all taste so good,
they make my tummy rumble.
Her cupcakes rule, but best of all,
is her awesome apple crumble.

When rain and lightning fill the sky,
and the thunder starts to crash.
We find a puddle and jump right in,
to make a great, big splash.

We run back home for cookies,
and warm milk to fill my tum.
Then, at bedtime, I get tucked in,
by the world's most magic mum!

Princess Daisy's Adventure

Princess Daisy loved fun and adventure, but she wasn't allowed to have any. When her brother, Prince Eric, rode off on his horse to have a good time with his friends, she had to stay at home and sew a pretty dress.

One day, Eric was getting on his horse, Bramble, to collect apples in the orchard. "Can I come, Eric?" Daisy pleaded. "Girls can't ride on their own," said Eric, galloping off. Sometimes Daisy wished she had been born a boy.

Daisy decided to follow Eric to the orchard on foot. When she reached it, she saw Bramble, but she couldn't see Eric. A moment later, she saw he was stuck up an apple tree, looking scared. "Whatever is the matter?" Daisy asked. "I was chased by a great, roaring MONSTER!" said Eric, his voice trembling. "Do you mean this great, roaring monster?" laughed Daisy, pointing to a little puppy that was sat by her feet. Prince Eric looked embarrassed. "I thought he was bigger," mumbled Eric. "Now I'm stuck up the apple tree!" "I'll help you down and then we can ride back on Bramble together," said Daisy.

"Please don't tell anyone about what happened today," begged Eric.
"Of course not," said Princess Daisy, as they arrived at the royal palace.
"You can play with me and my friends whenever you want," Eric told her.
Daisy hugged him. "You're the best brother in the world," she smiled.
"And you are the most fun sister," Eric said, hugging her back.
Then the little princess and the little prince picked up their
pretend swords and went off to have more adventures.

The Cheeky Pup

I have a pup who chews my laces,
And likes to hide in funny places.
When I saw him today I said,
"Why are you sleeping in my bed?"

The Little Wizard

I'm a little wizard,
I can do wizardly things.
I can make a frog a prince,
And give horses wings.
Don't you believe me?
Honestly, it's true.
And I could easily
Make a monkey out of you!

Moth and Butterfly

"Can that be an insect?"
Said Moth to Butterfly.
"It doesn't look like you or me,
And I don't think it can fly!"
Butterfly said, "You silly thing,
Look at its fancy clothes!
It's called a caterpillar,
Once you were one of those!"

The Frog and the Toad

"What are those black wriggly things?"
Toad asked his best friend, Frog.
They were relaxing by the lily pond,
Sitting on a wooden log.
"You ought to know!" Frog said to him,
Peering through the waters.
"They're called tadpoles,
And they're your sons and daughters!"

Goldy the Confused Hen

My little hen, called Goldy,
Thinks she is a cat.
She comes in through the cat flap,
What do you think of that?

Hedgehog in the Moonlight

If you see a hedgehog
Wandering on its own,
Don't go and pick it up,
Leave it well alone.
Its spikes are sharp,
And it could well bite.
Just leave it to wander happily,
Through the starry moonlight.

Little Batty Bat

A little bat called Batty
Is hanging by his toes.
He has two pointy ears,
And a shiny little nose.
He hangs around all day,
Without making a sound.
Then as soon as it is dark,
He wakes up and flies around.

Animal Pairs

Alligators and crocodiles
Are always very cheerful.
Monkeys and parrots
Are brave and never fearful.
Camels and lizards
Are always very loud.
And pandas and zebras
Always stand out in the crowd.

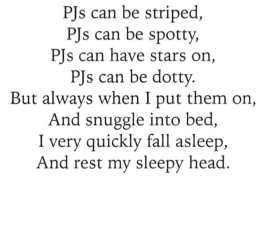

PJs

PJs can be striped,
PJs can be spotty,
PJs can have stars on,
PJs can be dotty.
But always when I put them on,
And snuggle into bed,
I very quickly fall asleep,
And rest my sleepy head.

Five Young Boys

Five young boys in sleeping bags,
Yellow, green and red.
They're on a camping holiday,
And now it's time for bed.

Snoring Until Morning

The night is still, the night is quiet,
There's just the sound of snoring.
Everyone is fast asleep and
They won't wake up until morning.

Fish Family Fun

Mother fish, daddy fish
And little fish, too,
Are all swimming around
In the ocean blue.

"Hello!" says a seal.
"I like those happy fish.
I hope they'll play with me,
That's my number one wish."

Little Fish

Big fish, long fish,
Pink fish and yellow
Want to chase the smallest fish,
Poor little fellow.

Little Fish says,
"I'd rather not be chased today.
I'll hide inside the nice pink shell,
Until the others go away."

Rocket Boy

I don't need a rocket
To travel up in space.
I've got a special suit instead,
With a helmet for my face.

I like it all alone up here,
I'm feeling very brave.
Shout loudly if you see me,
And don't forget to wave.

Journey Through Space

When I am an astronaut,
I'll zoom around the stars.
I'll walk across the moon,
And fly to Jupiter and Mars.

I won't go near the sun,
Because it's burning hot.
I think I'll stay in space,
I like it such a lot.

The Princess and the Gift

The princes and princesses
Have all gone to the fair.
There are rides and a helter-skelter,
And the big wheel if they dare!
The princess in the blue gown
Is so happy she could sing.
The prince has given her a gift.
Could it be a ring?

Silly Spring

I'm happy, happy, happy,
I want to jump and sing.
I'm picking flowers for my friends,
Because, at last, it's SPRING!

Goodnight, Mother Duck

Mother Duck, Mother Duck,
Paddling up a stream.
Where are you going?
And where have you been?

"I'm going home," said Mother Duck,
"While it's still light,
So I can cuddle my ducklings,
And kiss them goodnight."

Candyland

"YUCK!" said little Billy when he saw his tea one night.
His twin sister, Bella, wouldn't even take one bite.
She shook her head and said, "I wish we had SWEETS for tea!"
"Your wish might come true," said Billy. "Just follow me."
They went to the pantry and opened the door.
When they looked inside they couldn't believe what they saw.

Instead of shelves of vegetables, much to their surprise,
there was a secret hoard of candy, right before their eyes.
There were rivers made of chocolate and waterfalls of cream.
There were lollies, sweets and jellies, it was better than a dream!
"Let's explore!" cried Little Billy, pointing towards the wall.
"Wait for me!" yelled Bella. She could hardly wait at all.

There was a palace made of cookies,
and a valley made of sweets.
Ice creams towered over them,
as they walked down Candy Street.

Next, they bounced on a giant jelly,
and slid down Hot Fudge Hill.
They ate everything they wanted,
until they'd had their fill.

Feeling full they made a wish,
and closed their eyes up tight.
They found themselves back home again,
where everything felt right.

"That was the best adventure, EVER!"
said Billy, with a smile.
"Yes! It truly was," said Bella.
"But I don't want sweets for a while!"

The Brilliant Babysitter

"I don't want a babysitter," Danny said.
"I'd rather have Mother and Father instead."
Then Ruth arrived and there was quite a surprise.
She made magic happen in front of his eyes.

When Ruth waved her wand, all Danny's toys came alive.
His robots stood up and started to jive.
He laughed when his teddies bounced on the bed,
and his tiny toy planes flew right round his head.

"I'm hungry," said Danny, and Ruth just smiled.
With help from her wand, the whole kitchen went wild.
The knives, forks and saucepans flew around like mad,
to make the best dinner that Danny had ever had.

Danny's parents came back home, so Ruth said, "Goodbye!"
She waved her wand and flew up into the sky.
"Thanks, Ruth," said Danny. "I think you're really clever.
In fact, you're the best babysitter, ever!"

Teddy and Wuffy

Teddy and Wuffy are my best friends,
They come with me everywhere.
Wuffy is a woolly dog,
And Teddy is a bear.
Teddy sleeps with me at night,
And Wuffy Dog does too.
They love me best in the entire world.
They told me, so it's true!

Dad's Bird Table

On my dad's bird table,
The birds have all they need.
Seeds, nuts and breadcrumbs,
So they can come and feed.
There are sparrows, robins, finches,
Birds of each and every kind.
Dad loves to sit and watch them,
He says it soothes his mind.

Animal Holiday

The jungle animals are going away,
For a super skiing holiday.
Twenty days and twenty nights,
Away from the heat and jungle frights.
For snowball fights and lots of fun,
Climb on board, now, everyone!

Silly Savannah

Giraffes stretch their heads above the trees.
Ostriches look silly, with their knobbly knees.
Elephants plod, stomp, thump and rumble.
Monkeys run, skip, play and tumble.

The Mice and the Queen

Three tiny mice went to see the queen.
The queen asked, "Where have you been?"
The mice replied, "Where do we begin?
But first, can we please come in?"
"Yes," said the queen, "come inside.
I'll go and fetch some tasty cheese pies."

The Kittens and the Puppy

Two fluffy kittens playing on a wall.
Two fluffy kittens trying not to fall.
Puppy barked, "Catch me if you can!"
"Okay," said the kittens, so Puppy ran.
The kittens chased, but couldn't catch up,
So Puppy chased his tail. Funny little pup.

What Animals Do

Kitty Kitten loves to wash her face,
Bobby Bunny likes to run and race.
Betty Bee gets honey from the flowers,
Danny Duckling flies in stormy showers.
Willie Worm moves slower than a snail,
While Puppy Pumpkin chases his furry tail.

Biff the Baby Panda

Biff, the baby panda,
Climbs up a tree.
He calls to his mother,
"Quick, look at me!"
"Biff," calls Mother Panda.
"Come back down!
It's too high for you,"
She tells him, with a frown.

Autumn Fun

Summer has turned to autumn,
Leaves are blowing in the air.
The corn has all been gathered
For the harvest fair.

The windmill grinds the corn,
The baker bakes the bread,
And children eat it for their tea,
Before they go to bed.

Billy's Conkers

Billy Brown found some conkers
On a lovely autumn day.
Then he went and asked his dad
If he would like to play.
"This big one's mine," said Billy.
"I've put my name on top."
"This small one's mine," smiled Dad.
"Come on, give it a WHOP!"
Billy swung his conker,
And hit Dad's really hard.
"I've won!" cried Billy Brown,
As Dad's flew across the yard.

Autumn Explorers

"Let's go exploring,"
Says Tom to James one day.
"And collect some special things,
If we see some on our way."
The friends soon fill their baskets
With acorns, nuts and leaves.
"Hello, to you," greets Moley,
Popping up with one big heave.
High up in the meadow,
Two deer prepare to run.
"This is great," say Tom and James,
"Exploring is such fun!"

Treasure Hunt

Matt and Mike loved anything to do with pirates. They dressed up as pirates, and even built their own pirate ship. They were pirate mad! "I wish we were real pirates, finding real treasure," said Mike. "Maybe you can be," said Mother, handing them a piece of paper.

"It looks just like a map of our house," said Matt, squinting at the paper. Mother nodded. "That's right," she said. "You're going on a treasure hunt. Just follow the clues!" Matt and Mike studied the map. The first clue was a big red arrow pointing to their bedroom.

Matt and Mike raced upstairs. They opened cupboards and pulled out drawers, but they couldn't find the clue. They looked again at the map. "Look," said Mike. "There's an arrow pointing under the bed." They searched under the bed and found the next clue.

"X marks the spot where pirate gold is found.
The treasure is buried in the ground."

"In the garden!" they yelled, running outside. They searched everywhere and eventually found a black cross painted on the tree next to two spades and a gold key. They started digging, until suddenly they hit something. A treasure chest! Matt turned the key. CLICK! The chest opened. It was filled with chocolate coins wrapped in gold foil! "This is the very best type of pirate treasure!" said Matt and Mike. "Thanks, Mother!"

Two Little Puppies

Two little puppies,
Walking in the wood.
Two little puppies,
Trying to be good.
Along comes a tractor,
Making lots of noise.
The puppies bark and chase it,
Two naughty little boys!

Trampoline Fun

Two kittens and their puppy friend
Are jumping up so high.
If they jump up any higher,
They may just touch the sky.
Bouncing on a trampoline
Is such a lot of fun.
I bet they will be really tired,
Before the day is done.

Little Bouncing Puppy

My little pup can jump so high,
I think one day he'll reach the sky.
I'd like to jump as high as that,
But if I tried, I might fall flat.

Slimy Slug

I can't play the trombone,
I can't dance or sing.
I can't bounce on a trampoline,
I can only stick and cling.
There's not much I can do,
I can't even give you a hug.
Would you like to know why?
It's because I'm only a slimy slug!

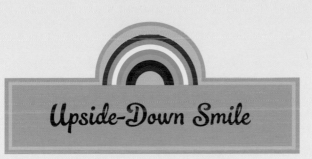

Upside-Down Smile

"Dad," I asked one day,
"Why does the rainbow frown?"
Dad said, "It doesn't, silly,
It's a smile that's upside down!"

Father and Son

Children have five fingers,
Children have five toes.
Children have two little ears,
And a very little nose.
Children have two big, round eyes,
That can be green, brown or blue.
Children also love their dads,
And their dads love them too.

Ballet Steps

Pretty little Charlotte
Is in her ballet dress,
Rehearsing her dance steps,
Trying to impress.
Her family want to join in,
And the dog would like to play.
But it's time for a quick drink,
Brought in tall glasses, on a tray.

Dancing Daisy

Daisy is a dancer,
She loves to pirouette.
Her shoes are made of satin,
Her dress is layers of net.
She holds her arms above her head,
And gets up on her toes.
Daisy is a super dancer,
And as perfect as a rose.

Fun in the Village

Barry the baker delivers his fresh bread.
John reaches for an apple just above his head.
Sarah fills the basket, so Mother can make a pie.
Two ducks wave their wings and say, "Hi!"

Planet Zog

Two alien brothers, from the planet Zog,
Came down to Earth and landed in a bog.
"Oh dear, this is squelchy," said one to the other.
"Let's fetch our special boots," replied his little brother.

Two Green Aliens

Once, two green children
Arrived from another planet.
The little boy was Billy-Bob,
The little girl was Janet.

They both thought Earth was strange,
And started to make a fuss.
They said, "Everyone is so different!
Why is no one green like us?"

Aliens

Aliens come in different sizes,
And they like to spring surprises.
But they won't win beauty prizes,
Even if they wear disguises!

Planet Zeus

Two slimy aliens,
From the planet Zeus,
One named Chris,
The other named Bruce.

They landed on planet Earth,
One lovely sunny day,
And liked it so much,
They decided they would stay.

Legs, Legs, Legs

Some aliens have six legs,
Some have three or four.
Human beings have only two,
It really is such a bore.

If I had lots of legs,
With lots and lots of feet,
I'd need lots and lots of shoes and socks,
And wouldn't that be neat?

Dancing Bears

Baby Bear and Mother Bear,
Dancing in the snow.
Mother Bear asks, "Want to stop?"
Baby Bear replies, "NO!"

Waddle, Waddle

Little penguins are so cute.
I love the way they waddle,
When they're running to the pool,
And wading out to paddle.
They wobble from side to side,
Like a bouncy rubber ball.
But even though they wobble,
They never seem to fall.

Daddy Penguins

Have you seen Daddy Penguin,
With a baby at his feet?
Baby Penguin sits so still,
He is so cute and sweet.
Mother Penguin looks for food,
While Daddy babysits.
I think that Daddy Penguin
Loves his little son to bits.

If I were a Fairy...

If I were a fairy, I'd have a dress
With ribbons and bows.
I would make magic spells
Whenever I twinkled my nose.

I'd have some lovely fairy wings
And a wand sparkly and bright.
I'd fly high up to Fairyland
On a soft and starry night.

Fizzy Spells

When fairies get together,
There is magic in the air.
Their wands fizz and sparkle,
And spells fly everywhere.

Toadstool Village

An elf lives in a toadstool house,
Next door to a little mouse.
A fairy lives across the street,
She keeps her toadstool nice and neat.
There's a sweet shop in the red toadstool,
In another there's a magic school.
Toadstool Village is very nice,
Say the elves, the fairies and the mice.

Magic Wishes

If you could have a fairy wish,
What would you ask for?
I know what I would want to have,
Twenty wishes more!

Princess Pippa's Pet

Princess Pippa had nobody to play with and was tired of being alone. "I need a pet!" she decided. "But not just any pet, an exciting one!" With that, she rushed off to find the royal butler, and asked him to order a crocodile.

The next day, Princess Pippa's new crocodile arrived, so she took him for a stroll in the palace gardens. They were having a lovely time, until the cheeky croc tried to steal some sausages!

The butler wasn't impressed with the naughty crocodile, so he sent it back to the swamp.

Princess Pippa's next pet was a penguin. He was very kind, and agreed to teach her how to skate.

They spent the entire morning spinning and jumping together. Princess Pippa had so much fun.

At lunchtime, the two new friends raced each other to the kitchen to find some food...

... but the greedy penguin got there first. Sure enough, the butler wasn't happy, and sent the penguin back.

The next day, Princess Pippa was eating her breakfast when four long legs wandered past the window. "My giraffe has arrived!" she gasped. "I can't wait to play with it."

Pippa ran excitedly up to the top of the castle, only to find the giraffe chomping on Queen Rose's red apples. "Send it back!" shouted Pippa. "These pets are just too exciting!"

Pippa was all alone again, and more lonely than ever. The butler didn't like
to see Pippa so sad, so he, King Leo and Queen Rose came up with a plan.
The next morning, a pretty box arrived with Pippa's name on it. She tore off the wrapping,
and there inside was the cutest, fluffiest kitten Pippa had ever seen. "Oh, thank
you so much," cried Pippa, cuddling it. "This is a really exciting pet!"

Little Chick's Big Adventure

One day, Little Chick and Mother Hen visited Horse, who was grazing near the forest. "What's it like in the forest?" asked Little Chick. "It's a very scary place," said Horse, with a shiver. "With very scary animals." "It's not safe for chicks," said Mother Hen. "Never go there alone." But this just made Little Chick more curious.

The next day, when Mother Hen was having her nap, Little Chick took
a tiny step towards the forest. Then another step, and another, until soon he was
looking up in amazement at all of the tall trees. He quickly made friends with some
fun bunnies and squirrels and played chase with them all afternoon until it was time
to leave. "The forest isn't scary at all!" decided Little Chick, as he waved
goodbye to his new friends and headed back home.

A hooting sound stopped Little Chick in his tracks.
Suddenly, a huge owl swooped down. "Are you lost?"
asked Owl. "I can show you the way home."

"Let me show you," said Fox, appearing
from behind a bush. He smiled widely at Little Chick,
showing his sharp teeth. Little Chick felt very afraid.

Just then, Little Chick heard clopping and clucking sounds.
It was Horse and Mother Hen! Horse cleared his throat and spoke in his
most polite voice. "We'll take Little Chick home, thank you!" he said.

When they were safely away from the forest, Mother Hen hugged her son.
"I was worried sick!" she told Little Chick. "Don't go off without me again."
"I promise I'll never go into the forest again!" replied Little Chick.
He had learned a big lesson.

If I Were...

If I were a pirate, I'd be fiercer than the rest.
I'd fight scary monsters and find treasure in a chest.

If I were a fairy,
I'd have lovely, fluttery wings.
I'd flit among the pretty flowers,
and dance in fairy rings.

If I were a princess, I'd have a kingdom of sweets.
I'd ride my royal pony, giving everybody treats.

If I were a baker, making cakes for a princess,
I'd bake the finest cakes while wearing a pretty dress.

If I were an explorer, going where no one had gone before,
I'd find a little dinosaur who growls and snarls and roars!

If I were a ballerina, I would wear my best tutu.
I'd show my ballet teacher all the steps that I could do.

If I were a magician, I'd do an amazing trick.
And make silver sparkles appear very quick!

But today I think I will just be me.
There's no one more fantastic that I could be.

Snow Stories

"Let's not build a snowman," Little Bear said.
"I've got a much better plan instead!
We'll make a snow spaceship and travel to Mars.
Let's zoom round the moon and then visit the stars."

"Let's play snow pirates," Little Bear roared.
"We'll go on a snow ship with treasure aboard.
We won't mind if the weather is icy and cold,
as long as we have all our huge bags of gold."

"Let's make a snow castle," Little Bear cried.
"We'll have turrets and thrones and a moat that is wide.
We'll be king and queen for the whole of the day.
People will have to do whatever we say!"

"Let's be snow explorers," Little Bear smiled.
"We can search for ice monsters that live in the wild.
We'll look for their footprints and track them and then,
tomorrow we'll do it all over again."

The Fairy Tree

Everything is magical
In this fairy tree of mine.
A magical door, a magical bird,
And a magical clothes line!

Kitchen Disaster

Oh dear! What a disaster!
The chef in the big white hat
Is going to drop the cake
When he trips over the cat!
The cook is rushing to the stove,
To save a boiling pot.
And the maid has burnt the shirt
Because the iron is too hot!

Time To Share

Once there was a little dinosaur called Bonny who had four best friends.
They had played together since they were baby dinosaurs and their play days
were great fun, until Bonny decided that she didn't want to share.

When everyone was playing at school one day, Bonny snatched the sparkly crown and wouldn't let anyone else take a turn.

Then, at the park, Bonny hogged the swing and the slide and took up the whole sandpit. Her friends were not happy.

Soon, it was time for a play day at Bonny's house.
"This is going to be fun!" she thought, waiting for the doorbell
to ring. But it didn't ring, and Bonny's friends all stayed away.
"It's because you won't share, Bonny," said Mum.
"Say sorry, and that will make everything right again."

So Bonny phoned each of her friends and said sorry.
They all came straight away, and had a brilliant time together.
After that, Bonny always remembered to share and play nicely,
and sometimes, if she'd been really good, she even
got to wear the sparkly crown.

The Mermaid who Wanted to Fly

Sitting on a rock in the middle of the sea, Ellie the mermaid heard a tiny cry. A baby crab had caught one of his claws in a crack in the rock. "Let me help," said Ellie, freeing him. All of a sudden, there was a whooshing sound, and a pink fish shot out of the water into the air, and then dived back down again!

Ellie swam straight after him. "Please can you teach me to fly?" she asked.
The pink fish smiled. "You'll need wings like mine," he said, twitching his fins.
Ellie looked down at her two little arms. "If I can find some wings by sunrise
tomorrow, will you promise to teach me how to fly?" she said.
"Yes, certainly," agreed the pink fish.

Ellie found lots of seaweed to use, and then asked the crabs to make her wings. "You helped our little baby, so we will help you," said the crabs, and they began weaving the seaweed together and snipping off the ends with their claws.

Soon enough, the crabs finished working and Ellie tried on her new wings. "Thank you so much!" she cried. "These are absolutely perfect. Now I will be able to fly in the sky just like the pink fish and all his flying friends!"

At sunrise, Ellie waited for the pink fish to appear. One by one, they flew
out of the water. "Come join us!" they called out to Ellie. She practised for hours,
diving into the sea, then flicking her tail to leap out of the water and into the air.
Before long, Ellie could fly higher than the pink fish. "Hooray!" they cried.
"Hooray for Ellie the amazing flying mermaid!"

Jungle Friends

Hippos, rhinos and crocodiles
Are fun, but can get snappy.
Monkeys, toucans and humming birds
Are nearly always happy.
Camels in the desert
Are always very calm.
And pretty little parrots
Are full of fun and charm.

Sleepy Animals

Elephants sleep standing up,
Purple, grey and brown.
Monkeys sleep the right way up,
But sloths sleep upside down!

Ollie's Slide

In Ollie Smith's back garden
There's a blue and yellow slide.
He loves to whizz down it,
And take Ted along for the ride!

Ollie's Teddy Bear

I am a cuddly teddy bear,
I am Ollie's best toy.
I am his special teddy
And he's my special boy.
Today we're playing on a swing,
It's like flying through the air.
It's nice being on our own,
Just a boy and his teddy bear.

The Fairy and the Three Wishes

Fairy Sunshine was loved by everyone because she was so sweet and kind.
One day, on her way to school, she spotted Dormouse sat on a stone.
"I have a sore foot, so I can't fetch water," he said, sadly. Fairy Sunshine
reached for Dormouse's acorn cup. "I'll get some for you," she said.

After fetching the water, Fairy Sunshine flew on, but then spotted Bluebird crying. "I need to build a new nest, but I've hurt my wing," he sobbed. Fairy Sunshine quickly picked lots of twigs and made Bluebird a comfy nest.

The helpful fairy went on her way, but stopped when she saw Honeybee sneezing. "Achoo! I can't work because of my cold," the bee explained. "I will find some pollen for you," said Fairy Sunshine, kindly.

After helping all her friends, Fairy Sunshine finally arrived at school and flew straight to her desk. Mrs Heatherfly had a special test for each of her magical students, and promised to grant three wishes to whoever got top marks.

Fairy Sunshine tried her very hardest and sure enough, came top of the class! The kind fairy knew exactly what to ask for. "I wish for Dormouse's foot to get better, for Bluebird's wing to heal, and for Honeybee's cold to go away."

Mrs Heatherfly granted each of Fairy Sunshine's wishes and then allowed her another, for being so thoughtful. "I'd like a party," said Fairy Sunshine, in her most polite voice. With a wave of her wand, Mrs Heatherfly magically conjured up a party.

Dormouse, Bluebird and Honeybee were all feeling much better, and had a fantastic time dancing with Fairy Sunshine and all her fairy friends. Everyone agreed that Fairy Sunshine was incredibly kind and thoughtful, and a fabulous dancer, too!

My Best Friend

My best friend is special to me.
She comes to play and we have some tea.
We sit on the grass, with our toys in the sun.
We don't need anyone else to have fun.

She makes up brilliant games to play,
and we laugh together every day.
I love the smile on her pretty face,
I know she's someone I can never replace.

Whenever I'm poorly we talk for hours.
She brings me treats and lovely flowers.
She cheers me up with a joke or game,
and if she were poorly, I'd do the same.

We always stay up when it's time for bed,
and play for five more minutes instead.
The thing I love best is that we're always together.
Better still is knowing we'll be friends forever.

Pretty Polly

I've got a little parrot,
She's really bright and jolly.
She flies around my bedroom,
Her name is Pretty Polly.

I'm teaching her to whistle,
It won't take very long.
And when she gets as good as me
We'll sing a funny song.

Clever Trevor

I have a big dog called Trevor,
Who really is very clever.
He can sit, stand and run around,
Even his bark makes a lovely sound.

Naughty Pup

Pauly Pup is one year old,
He's very cheeky, and won't be told.
When Kitty Cat comes strolling in,
Pauly Pup barks to make her spin.
But nobody minds his cheekiness,
Even when he's making mess.
Because Pauly Pup is cute and happy,
He's such an adorable little chappy.

Puppy Pal

I'm never lonely with my dog,
He's always by my side.
He knows just where to find me,
Even when I try to hide!

Maisy's Daisy

Maisy, Maisy, has lost her daisy,
Where could it have gone?
High and low, low and high,
She searches the whole day long.

Princess Playroom

The princess in the playroom
Is playing happily.
Soon she'll make her little doll
Something nice for tea.

Her hair is long and golden,
Her eyes are baby blue.
She wears a tiara on her head
And her dress is pretty, too.

Messy Playtime

I've got glitter in my hair
And glue stuck to one knee.
I've got paint on both my ankles,
There's stuff all over me!
I've got gravy stains all down my front
And ice cream on my dress.
Dad says, "Charlotte, really,
You look such a mucky mess!"

Fairy Wishes

I wish I was a fairy,
With soft and shiny wings,
Waving a magic wand
And doing magic things.
I would fly high up to Fairyland,
To see the fairy queen.
Then I'd tell all my friends
About everything I had seen.

I Wish...

If I could wish upon a star,
I'd wish that someone from afar
Would come and take me by the hand
And fly with me to distant lands,
Show me dragons, dinosaurs and kings,
And magicians doing magical things.

The Scarlet Rocket

Tommy is a train driver, he drives the Scarlet Rocket.
He races it along a track, with a whistle in his pocket.
As the train gets near the station, Tommy blows his whistle hard.
Then the train chugs to a halt, and the doors are opened by the guard.
TOOT! goes Tommy's whistle as more passengers go inside.
There are lots of comfy seats, so come and have a ride!

My Pretty Lamb

Woolly Sam, my pretty lamb,
Has followed me to school.
My friends all want to pet him,
They think he's super cool.

He shouldn't really be here.
He should be at home with Mum.
She'd be giving him his morning milk,
And tickling his tum.

The Great Escape

Farmer Claire was trying to cheer up her animals on Willow Tree Farm. Rodney the horse was tired of his stable, Millicent the cow complained about the cowshed and Lulu the sheep was sick of her pen! "What we need is some adventure," said Rodney. Everyone agreed, but what adventure? The very next day they had the answer. A travelling circus was driving right by the farm. "That's it!" said Rodney. "We'll run away and join the circus!" So, they all tiptoed off the farm when Farmer Claire was busy planting some flowers.

At the circus, the big tent was already up, so the animals went inside. Millicent asked the ringmaster, "Please can we join the circus?" "Okay," he said, "but you need to work on your acts first." The animals knew exactly what they wanted to do. Lulu would be a trapeze artist, Rodney a show horse and Millicent an acrobat. They were sure it just meant a bit of prancing and bouncing, with a bit of swinging as well. It would be easy!

BIG TOP CIRCUS

"Time to rehearse!" called the ringmaster. Rodney cantered round and
round the ring until he was dizzy. Millicent fell off the trampoline and Lulu
found out she was afraid of heights! For the next few days, they rehearsed all day and
performed each night, until the animals were so tired they could hardly stand up!

"I want a good show tonight!" the ringmaster told them. "No more mistakes!"
"I miss Farmer Claire," said Rodney.
"We do, too!" said Millicent and Lulu.

That night, the crowd cheered as Rodney cantered around the ring, and Millicent
did her best to stay on the trampoline. Then came the big last act. The Flying Lulu!
Just then, Lulu saw Farmer Claire in the front row and immediately lost her grip. She fell
onto the trampoline and BOING! She bounced up, landing SPLAT! on Rodney's back.

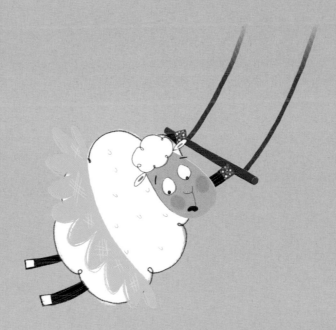

"I think you would be better off back at the farm!" said the ringmaster.
The animals agreed, and soon they were back, eating and lazing in the sun again.
"Welcome home," said Farmer Claire, smiling happily.

Sweet Dreams

I'm snuggling up to Teddy,
In my comfy bed.
Stripy Cat is curled up, too.
I have nice dreams in my head.

Sleepyhead

It's time for bed, sleepyhead, snuggle up tight.
I hope you have sweet dreams, all through the night.
In the morning, Mother will kiss you and say,
"Wake up, sweetiepie, it's a beautiful day."

Party Bells

It's party time, it's party time,
Soon the bells will start to chime.
We're in the woods, as you can see,
So won't you come and dance with me?

Fairy Invite

Everyone at the party has come from really far.
There's music playing, from a fairy guitar!
Come along and join in all the fun and games.
Meet the fairies and learn all their names!

The Princess and the Lost Crown

Princess Sophie was naughty and spoilt. If she wanted something, she screamed until she got it. If she wanted ice cream, she had ice cream. If she wanted to wear pink boots, she wore pink boots. If anyone dared to say no, the naughty princess just screamed and screamed and screamed, until they gave in.

One day, the king suggested they go to the beach, so they set off with all their servants in lots of royal carriages. When they arrived, they put up a little tent for Sophie to change in and, while she and her maid went inside, the others waited nervously, hoping this would be a tantrum-free day.

When Princess Sophie came out of the tent, she was wearing her swimsuit
and her little crown. "Sophie," said the queen, "please leave your crown here, or
you might lose it." Sophie opened her mouth to scream. "Oh, alright then!" said the
queen, quickly, embarrassed by her daughter's naughtiness. Sophie stomped off,
pleased to have got her own way again. The king followed his daughter into
the sea, just in time to see her get splashed by a big wave. When he picked
her up, spluttering and gasping, her crown was no longer on her head.
It had disappeared into the sea.

Everyone held their breath and waited for Sophie's tantrum to begin.
Sure enough, the spluttering soon turned to screaming. "I'M ALL WET!"
the princess screamed, and then she put her hands to her head. "WHERE IS
MY CROWN! Find it NOW, or I shall scream ALL DAY!" So, everyone began to
look this way and that. Boats were launched, fishing nets were thrown into the sea
and divers searched the seabed, but there was no sign of the tiny royal crown.
Then, someone shouted, "I've found something!" But it was only an old teapot.

This time, Princess Sophie was really upset. She didn't scream, or throw a tantrum, she just sobbed. The queen picked her up and cuddled her. "My lovely crown," sobbed Sophie into her mother's shoulder. "I love it so much. If you ever find it, I promise I will never be naughty again." Just then, one of the servants pointed out to sea. A crab was climbing onto a rock and, hooked round his claw, was Princess Sophie's missing crown!

Princess Sophie smiled with joy and hugged her parents. From that day on she was the nicest, best-behaved little girl anyone could wish for.

Honey for Tea

Mummy Bear and Daddy Bear,
And their family,
Are in a pretty meadow,
With bread and honey for their tea.

Two little cubs are playing chase,
Three more sit on the rug,
And cuddly little Baby Bear,
Gives Mum a special hug.

Another bear is watching,
He's feeling hungry, too.
"Come and join us," says Mummy Bear.
"There's plenty here for you."

Teddy's Day

If you go into the woods,
You'll see teddies everywhere.
Some are sitting on the grass,
Some have brought a special chair.

They are having a tea party,
With lots of yummy food.
And all the bears are happy,
And in a jolly mood.

What can they be celebrating,
To bring so many here?
I think it must be Teddy's Day,
It happens every year!

Teddy Dance

Round in a circle,
Dance the fluffy teddy bears.
This way and that way,
Wiggling here and there.

They dance into the middle,
And do some little twirls.
Then the little boy teddies,
Ask to dance with all the girls.

Little Mo

I always take my pretty doll
Everywhere I go.
She's really cute and sweet,
And her name is Little Mo.

We're swinging in an orchard,
There are apples on the trees.
The flowers move their pretty heads,
In the gentle summer breeze.

Party Food

Party food is special,
Party food is fun.
Party food is tasty,
When it's in my tum!

Princess Party

Today there are decorations all about,
With a cake and candles to blow out.
My friends have come for birthday tea.
What a lovely day. I'm as happy as can be.

Swinging Monkeys

Monkeys eat bananas
And swing between the trees
They have long and bendy tails
And little knobbly knees!

Bananas for Tea

Can you see the monkeys,
Hanging in the trees?
They've got big smiles on their faces,
And bananas for their tea.

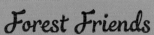

Forest Friends

"Come for a stroll," said Mother Rabbit,
One bright and sunny day.
"Put on your new blue jacket,
And let's go straight away."

"Hello, Frog," called Little Rabbit.
"Have you had your morning swim?"
He was happy seeing all his friends,
And they were happy to see him.

Camping Fun

I'm camping in the garden,
With my friend from next door.
We're having such a lot of fun,
And tomorrow we'll have some more!

Just the Spot

Here's a good place to make our camp,
It's not too dry and it's not too damp,
There's a good branch to hang our lamp.
On a lovely summer day,
It's difficult to get things right,
To be cool by day and warm by night.
But we think this is a terrific site,
For our camping holiday.

Starlit Supper

It's such a great adventure,
Camping with your greatest friends.
I'm having so much fun,
I hope it never ends!
We toast marshmallows on the fire,
And eat sausages for tea.
I hope you enjoyed this camping trip,
Just as much as me!

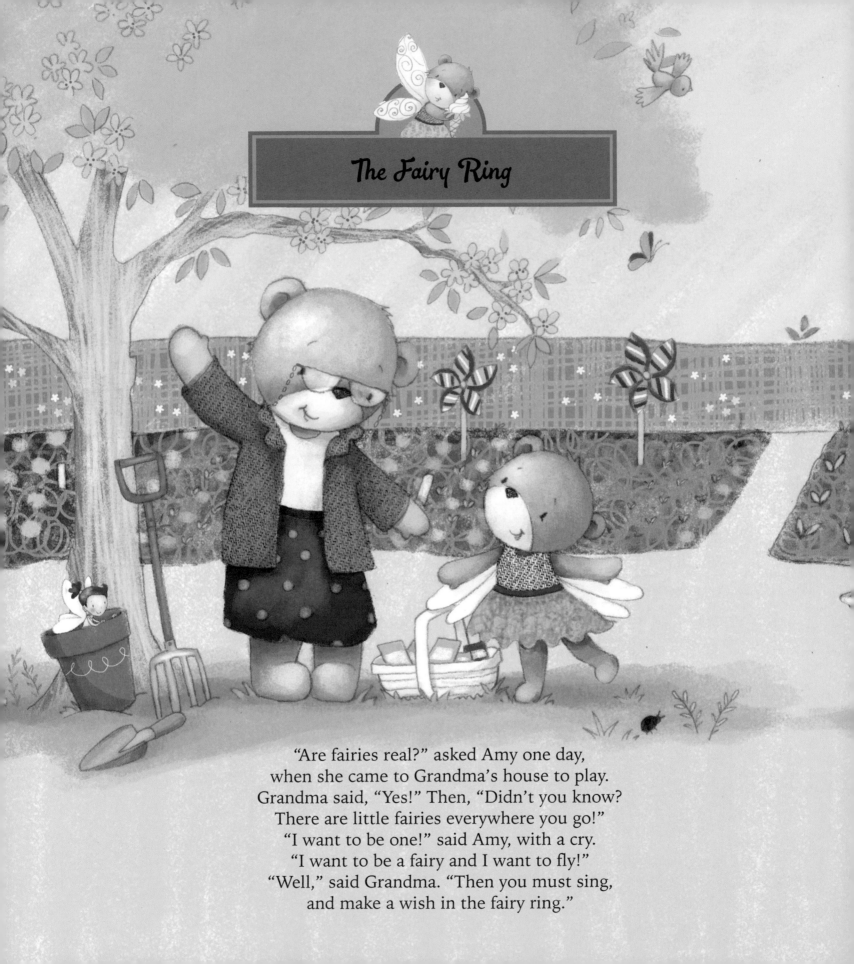

The Fairy Ring

"Are fairies real?" asked Amy one day,
when she came to Grandma's house to play.
Grandma said, "Yes!" Then, "Didn't you know?
There are little fairies everywhere you go!"
"I want to be one!" said Amy, with a cry.
"I want to be a fairy and I want to fly!"
"Well," said Grandma. "Then you must sing,
and make a wish in the fairy ring."

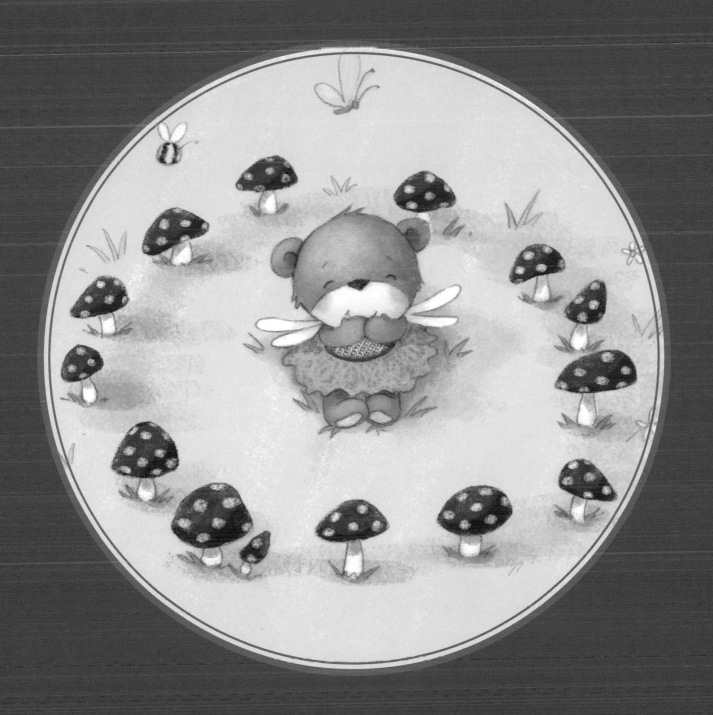

As Grandma went off to have a rest,
Amy put her wishing to the test.
In the fairy ring, with her eyes closed tight,
Amy sang and wished with all her might.
At last, there came a tinkling sound,
and little fairies flew all around.
They waved their wands and took Amy by the hand.
"Let's go!" they cried. "Come to Fairyland!"

In Fairyland, Amy saw wonderful things,
and before she knew it, Amy had wings!
She zoomed and darted here and there.
"Woo-hoo!" cried Amy, as she whizzed through the air.
She found the prettiest tree house she had ever seen.
It was the magic palace of the Fairy Queen.

The Fairy Queen showed Amy all around.
Then they gently fluttered down to the ground.
"Let's have a fairy feast," the Fairy Queen said.
"Then after that, it will be time for bed."
"Thank you, fairies," whispered Amy, and off she ran.
"What an amazing adventure. I can't wait to tell Gran!"

It's a Goal!

The players in the red shirts,
Are really strong and tall.
And the players in the blue shirts,
Are very, very small.
But the smaller team is winning,
They are quicker than the rest.
And Hedgehog gets past everyone,
His goalscoring skills are best!

Pink and Blue

We're two little monsters, pink and blue.
There are lots of fun things we like to do.
We play on the swings and the see-saw, too.
I bet we do all the same things as you!

Screaming Jimmy

Little Jimmy yells so loud,
He's almost ready to pop.
His parents don't know what to do,
To make Little Jimmy stop.
"Why is he screaming?" asks Mother.
"His cheeks are rosy-red.
I only asked him nicely,
If he would go to bed."

Jack and the Sea

The sandy beach that goes down to the sea,
is Jack and his dad's special place to be.
They love to eat ice cream in the hot sun.
When it melts and runs, it is part of the fun.

In the clear rock pools where Jack loves to splash,
strange, tiny creatures all wriggle and dash.
Jack sees starfish and seahorses as well.
There are limpets on rocks and shiny shells.

Jack and his dad like to look for fish,
whose silvery tails wiggle with a swish.
They dive down to where the hermit crabs creep,
and the old sea turtle swims in the deep.

Jack loves to play in the sand for hours,
making sandcastles with moats and towers.
There's no other place Jack would rather be,
than having fun with his dad by the sea.

Sneak Attack

It was past his bedtime, but Archie wanted his football. The problem was, it was downstairs in the locked living-room cupboard, and his parents were having a dinner party. Plus, his big brother, Steve, was in the hallway. Archie would have to get past him first.

Using his fishing rod, Archie
carefully lowered a bag of
Super-choc Sweets. When Steve
noticed it, he was amazed.
"Wow," he said, bending down.
Quick as a flash, Archie sneaked
down the stairs and into the kitchen.

Archie found the cupboard key and
then looked in the kitchen drawers.
"Now for the fun part," said Archie.
He took a lifelike toy snake from the
drawers and slid it slowly under the
door that led into the living room.

Suddenly, there was a loud scream. "SNAAAKE!"
cried one of the guests. Archie opened the door
and giggled as the grown-ups ran out of the room.
When the coast was clear, Archie dashed in,
unlocked the cupboard and found his best ball.

Archie grinned and turned round to see Mother, Father, Steve and the party guests staring at him. "Anyone for football?" he asked, cheekily.

"Bedtime, Archie,"
said Mother, taking the ball.
"Never mind," said Archie.
"There's always tomorrow."

Garden Adventures

I'm exploring in my garden,
It's going to be such fun.
I've got some food and drink,
And a hat to shade me from the sun.

My Pet Chameleon

I've lost my pet chameleon.
It looks exactly like what it's climbing on.
I've looked and looked, and I can't be certain,
But I think it's climbing up the curtain.

Rock Pools

I'm busily exploring, on holiday,
Looking in the rock pools around the bay.
I've caught lots of crabs and so has my friend Jack,
We keep them in a bucket, then we put them back.

The Slimy Slug Burger

Pete was a fan of some types of bugs.
He liked spiders and beetles, but he didn't like slugs.
Slugs were too slithery and slimy and chilly.
"You're scared of slugs?" teased his sister. "How silly!"

"I'll show her," thought Pete. "Just you wait!"
So, he went to the kitchen and took out a plate.

He cut ten slimy hot dogs to a slug's shape and size.
For the eyestalks, each sausage slug got a pair of French fries.

Pete put the fake slugs inside a big bun.
"The perfect slug burger," he said. "Now for some fun."
He looked for his sister and showed her the treat.
"Mmm, garden-fresh slugs that I can't wait to eat!"

Pete opened his mouth and took a big bite.
His little sister screamed and ran off in fright.

"That showed her," said Pete. "What an excellent plot!"
The sausage slugs were so tasty that Pete scoffed the lot.

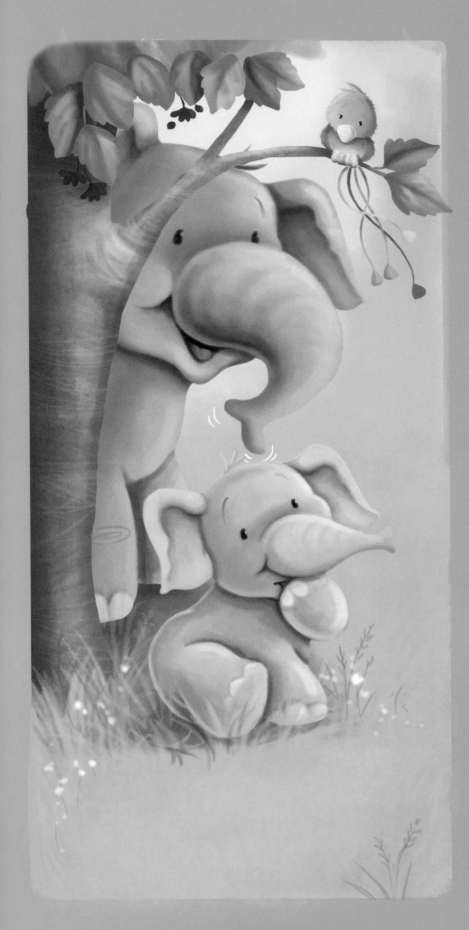

Trunk Tale

A little baby elephant,
Sheltering from the sun,
Standing in the shade,
Underneath his mum.
"Mum," asked baby elephant,
"Why haven't I got a nose?"
"You've got a trunk instead," said Mum,
"So you can touch your toes."

Pip the Elephant

Pip the elephant loved to play,
Her best game was hide-and-seek.
Pip closed her eyes and counted to ten,
While Mummy told her not to peek.

Happy Farm

Little lambs have wriggly tails,
Little hens like pecking snails.
Little calves skip and run,
Little pigs like having fun.
The farmyard is a happy place,
Even the cat has a smiley face.
Life on the farm is never dull,
The animals think it's wonderful.

The Farmer's Men

A cat, a hen, a pig, a pen,
A cow, a sow and a lamb of course.
These are things the farmer's men,
Need on a farm, besides a horse.

Imagination Island

Pirates Meet the Queen

I'm playing with my brother,
Because we've just had our tea.
The box is a pirate ship,
And the carpet is the sea.
I've got a pirate telescope,
And a hat upon my head.
And when we've finished playing,
We'll have to go to bed.

Two little pirates
Went to see the queen.
The queen said, "You're late!
Where have you been?"
The pirates said, "Your majesty,
Where do we begin?"
The queen said, "Oh never mind,
Won't you please come in?"

Jungle Weather

It's never dry in the jungle,
There is such a lot of rain.
It rains and rains all through the day,
And at night it rains again.

The jungle has no winter,
Spring and autumn it has not.
It's always summer where we live,
And that makes it very HOT!

Flower Power

Fairies painting pretty flowers,
Showing off their magic powers.
Watch them flying high and low.
Make a wish before they go!

Rainbow Wishes

A pretty little fairy,
Curtsies to her queen.
She's going to make a rainbow,
Blue, yellow, pink and green.
She has a pouch of fairy dust,
And a magic wand to hold.
WHOOSH! She makes a rainbow,
And a pot of gold!

Time for Bed

"The moon is up," Blue Teddy said,
Pointing to the sky.
"That means it must be time for bed,"
Said Pink Teddy, with a sigh.
"Bedtime is the very best,"
Said Blue Teddy with a beam.
"That's when we can both snuggle up,
And dream a lovely dream."

The Princess and the Farm

Princess Melanie enjoyed eating breakfast. She always had a bowl of cereal with creamy milk, followed by a boiled egg with buttery soldiers to dip in the yolk. "Yummy!" she said, when she took her first bite each day.

She had just started eating one morning when a fluffy, yellow ball on tiny legs ran by. "Whatever is that?" she exclaimed, as the fluffy, yellow ball on tiny legs disappeared out of the door and into the garden.

"Wait for me!" cried Princess Melanie. The little ball of fluff turned to look at her with big, round eyes, then it slipped through a hedge towards a group of big buildings. "I wonder who lives there?" thought Princess Melanie.

Panting slightly, Princess Melanie reached a wooden fence
where a girl was standing. The fluffy, yellow ball was sat at her feet.

"Can you tell me what that is?" asked Princess Melanie. The girl laughed.
"It's a chick, your highness. When she grows up she'll be a chicken and lay eggs.
We have lots on the farm. My name is Daisy, let me show you around."

First, Daisy took Princess Melanie to see the cows.
"They give us lovely, creamy milk," explained Daisy.
"I have milk on my cereal every day," said Princess Melanie.

In the orchard, Daisy picked up a chicken. "This is Henny," she said.
"She lays big, brown eggs." Princess Melanie's eyes lit up.
"I love eating boiled eggs for breakfast," she said. "Can I be your friend
and help you collect the eggs?" Daisy hugged the princess.
"I'd like that more than anything," she said. Now the two girls are always
together on the farm, and they have become the best of friends.

The Frog Prince

Once there was a princess who had a beautiful golden ball.
One day, while she was playing, the golden ball fell into a lake and
sank to the bottom. The princess began to cry.

A frog heard her sobs. "Why are you crying?" he asked.
"My golden ball has sunk to the bottom of the lake," wept the princess.
"If I get it, will you promise to give me anything I ask?" said the frog.
"Anything," the princess promised.

"I want to sit at your table, eat off your plate and
sleep in your bed," said the frog, as he prepared to dive into the lake.
"I promise to give you what you ask," said the princess. So the frog swam
to the bottom of the lake and got the golden ball. But when he gave it
to the princess, she snatched the ball away and ran
back to the castle as fast as she could.

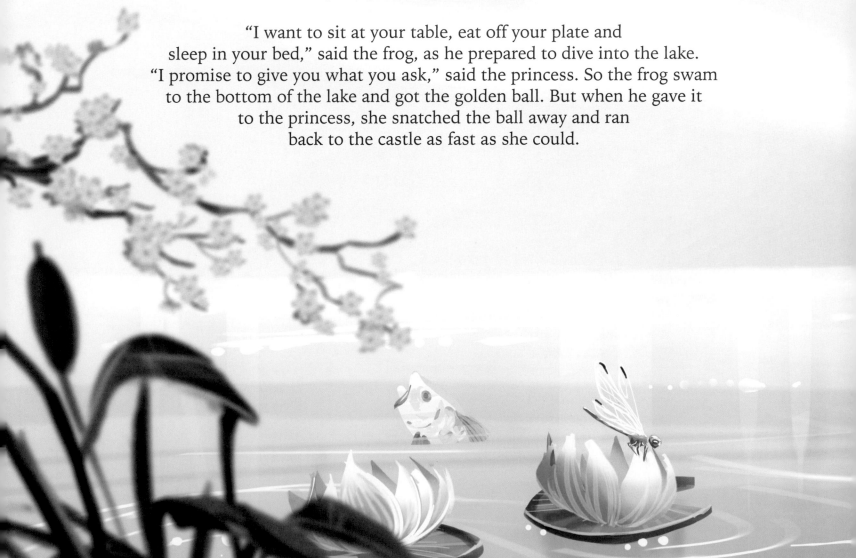

Back at the castle, the princess and the king were eating supper when the frog appeared. "Who are you?" asked the king. The princess explained to him about the frog and her promise. "A promise cannot be broken," said her father. So the princess shared her supper with the frog.

Later that evening, the frog appeared in her bedroom. "No!" the princess cried, as he hopped onto the bed, but she had to obey the king and keep her promise. So the frog slept on a soft white pillow next to her.

In the morning the frog was still there. "Princess, if you would kiss me just once," said the frog. "I will go away and leave you alone." Wanting to get rid of him, the princess screwed up her face and kissed the slimy frog. "Ugh!" she said and she threw the pillow, with the frog on it, across the room.

For a while there was silence. The princess was worried she had hurt the frog. "Are you alright?" The answer came not in a croak, but in a deep, warm voice. "Yes I am, princess," it said, and standing before her was a handsome young man. The young man told the princess that a witch had cursed him and turned him into a frog. Only the kiss of a princess could break the spell and change him back into a prince. The princess fell in love with the prince and it wasn't long before they married, and they both lived happily ever after.

Space Snooze

Billy Brown is dreaming,
He's an astronaut in space.
Peeping through the rocket's window,
Can you see his facc?
I wonder, in the morning,
If he'll remember where he's been?
And tell all of his friends,
About his super-awesome dream.

Tiny Traveller

When I dream I'm in my rocket ship,
And the Earth is far beneath me.
I can spot huge lakes and mountains,
Long rivers and the sea.
But I can't see any houses,
Or buildings, big and tall.
And I can't see any people,
Because they are far too small.

Pet Party

Kitten and parrot, monkey and mouse,
Are having a party at Charlie's house.
There are wobbly jellies, yellow and red,
And a penguin is sitting on Sarah's head.

Birthday Tea

I'm going to a party,
My friends will all be there.
I've a pretty pink dress,
And ribbons for my hair.
I've chosen a nice present,
And wrapped it carefully.
There will be cake and lots of candles,
And sandwiches for tea.

The Silver Ballgown

Fairy Freckles was sitting in the sunshine, resting. She was new to the forest and didn't know anyone. She was about to fly back home when a fairy in a blue dress flew up to her. "Hello, I'm Raindrop," the fairy said. "Are you coming to the fairy ball tomorrow?" Fairy Freckles shook her head. "I don't have a ballgown to wear," she said, shyly. Raindrop smiled. "Meet me here tomorrow and you can make one."

When Fairy Freckles met Raindrop the next day, she had three friends with her. "This is Fairy Snowflake, Fairy Moonbeam and Fairy Sunray," said Raindrop, introducing them all. "We are going to make our dresses too, but why don't you go first?" Nervously, Fairy Freckles waved her tiny wand, but all it could magic up was a plain, boring, grey dress. "Oh dear!" giggled Fairy Snowflake, unkindly. "That will never do for the fairy ball!" Fairy Freckles flew off embarrassed and upset.

Fairy Freckles flew deep into the forest and met a spider. "Let me help you make your dress," said the friendly spider. The spider flung the boring grey dress onto her web and began spinning furiously. Fairy Freckles watched in awe and soon, the dress was covered with swirling strands of silver spider thread. "It's beautiful," said Fairy Freckles. "Thank you so much!"

Fairy Freckles changed into her new silver ballgown and flew as fast as she could to the ball. When she arrived, all the other fairies turned to look at her. They gasped when they saw her sparkly, silver dress. "It's the most beautiful gown at the ball!" cried Raindrop. The other fairies agreed. "We're sorry we were unkind to you," said Fairy Snowflake. "That's okay," replied Freckles. Then they danced together for the rest of the evening.

Just like Dad

Tom loved his dad. He wanted to be just like him.
"I'll go and help in the garden," said Tom. "I'll wear my
best boots and water the flowers, just like Dad."

Tom turned on the hosepipe and the water went SWOOSH!
It wiggled and jiggled everywhere. Tom was soaked.
"Oh, no," he said. "I'm all wet."

Tom's boots went squelch, squelch, as he walked inside.
He put on Dad's big, blue jumper and comfy slippers, but when he
looked in the mirror, he felt silly. Dad's clothes were far too big.

Tom gave up and slumped into Dad's chair in the living room.
He turned on the TV and read a comic. Then, Mother came in and laughed.
"You look just like your dad," she said. Tom smiled happily.

Princess Polly's Birthday

In a castle on a tall hill, lived a little princess called Polly. It would soon be her birthday, but poor Princess Polly didn't have many friends. The castle was far, far away and she was worried that no one would come to her birthday party. The day before her birthday, Princess Polly walked past a door and heard laughter.

Inside, she saw a little girl and a lady sewing a yellow dress. "My name is Anna, your highness," said the little girl. "This is my mother. She's the royal dressmaker."

"I would love a beautiful yellow dress like that," sighed Princess Polly.

Anna looked at her mother and smiled.

Just then, a boy ran past. "Why are you running?" Princess Polly asked. "My name is Joe," he said. "I'm taking a special order for a pair of golden shoes to my father, who is the royal shoemaker."

Princess Polly then arrived at the kitchen, where two girls were baking. "We're Jenny and Penny," they said. "We're making a special cake with our mother, who is the royal cook." "I'd love to taste it when it's ready," said Princess Polly.

Next, Princess Polly went into the garden. A boy was tending the roses. "Who are you?" she asked. "I'm Tom. I've grown these beautiful roses," he said, letting her smell one. "They must be for someone very special," sighed the princess.

That night, Princess Polly decided to invite all the children she had met that day to her party. In the morning, she saw the yellow dress and golden shoes near her bed. She laughed with delight and ran through the castle calling, "Anna, Joe, Jenny, Penny, Tom, you are all invited to my party!"
"Hooray! We'd love to come, thank you, Princess."

That afternoon, wearing the beautiful yellow dress made by Anna's mother, and the golden shoes made by Joe's father, Princess Polly had her party. On the table were the red roses from Tom and the yummy cake made by Jenny and Penny. "Thank you for coming and making today so special," laughed Princess Polly, as she hugged her new friends. "Now, let's have a wonderful time!"

Little Fairies

Little fairies love to play,
They love to dance and sing.
They fly up high with the butterflies,
On their pretty fairy wings.
They love to sit among the flowers,
On a soft and sunny day.
Listening to the bumblebees,
And what they have to say.

Birthday Picnic

"What a lovely day this is,"
Said Fairy Twinkletoes.
"A birthday picnic in the woods,
And presents tied with bows."

Fairy Flowers

I wonder if this fairy,
Will use her magic powers,
To change the frog into a prince,
Or perhaps a bunch of flowers?